D1439092

THE WAYSIDE
AND WOODLAND
𝔐 𝔐 SERIES

WAYSIDE AND WOODLAND
TREES

Pl. I.

Flowers of Horse Chestnut.

Wayside and Woodland Trees

Trees

A POCKET GUIDE TO THE BRITISH SYLVA

BY

EDWARD STEP, F.L.S.

AUTHOR OF
"WAYSIDE AND WOODLAND BLOSSOMS"
"WAYSIDE AND WOODLAND FERNS" "ANIMAL LIFE OF THE BRITISH ISLES"
ETC.

WITH 175 PLATES, 24 OF WHICH IN COLOUR AND 151 FROM
PHOTOGRAPHS BY HENRY IRVING AND THE AUTHOR
ALSO 57 TEXT FIGURES BY MABEL E. STEP

LONDON
FREDERICK WARNE & CO. LTD.
AND NEW YORK

(*All rights reserved*)

"*Of all man's works of art, a cathedral is greatest.   A vast and majestic tree is greater than that.*"

Henry Ward Beecher

PRINTED IN GREAT BRITAIN

PREFACE.

THE purpose of this volume is not the addition of one more to the numerous treatises upon sylviculture or forestry, but to afford a straightforward means for the identification of our native trees and larger shrubs for the convenience of the rural rambler and Nature-lover. The list of British arborescent plants is a somewhat meagre one, but all that could be done in a pocket volume by way of supplementing it has been done—by adding some account of those exotics that have long been naturalized in our woods, and a few of more recent introduction that have already become conspicuous ornaments in many public and private parks.

In this edition forty-eight extra plates have been added, of which twenty-four are in colours. The latter are in part reproductions of water-colour studies of flowers and fruits, and partly from photographs by a new method. For the black and white plates, the photographs, it should be explained, have been taken upon a novel plan in most cases. This consists in photographing a deciduous tree in its summer glory, and returning to the same spot in winter and photographing the same individual, so that a striking comparison may be made between the summer

and winter aspects of the principal species. Supplementary
photographs are given, in many cases, of the bole, which exhibit
the character of the bark, and should prove a valuable aid in
the identification of species. Others show in larger detail the
flowers or fruit, and the characteristic leaf-buds in spring.

The figures in the text have all been expressly drawn for the
work with a view to showing at a glance the general character
of the foliage, and in most cases the flower and fruit.

The work is divided into two sections. Part I. including
those species that are generally considered to be indigenous
to the British Islands, with briefer notices of the introduced
species that are closely related to them. Part II. being devoted
to those of foreign origin, some of them introduced so long ago
that they are commonly regarded as native by those who are
not botanists.

INTRODUCTORY.

———◆———

THERE are two points of view from which to regard trees—the mercantile and the æsthetic. The former is well exemplified in Dumbiedyke's advice to Jock : " Jock, when ye hae naething else to do, ye may be aye sticking in a tree ; it will be growing, Jock, when ye're sleeping." The canny Scot was thinking of the "unearned increment" another generation might gather in, due to the almost unceasing activity of the vegetable cells in the manufacture of timber. The other view was expressed by " the Autocrat of the Breakfast-table " in a letter to a friend : " Whenever we plant a tree we are doing what we can to make our planet a more wholesome and happier dwelling-place for those who come after us, if not for ourselves." But, after all, it is the trees that have been planted by Nature that give the greatest pleasure apart from commercial considerations—the lonely Pine, that grows in rugged grandeur on the edge of the escarpment where its seed was planted in the crevice by the wind ; the Oak that grows outside the forest, where a squirrel or a jay dropped the acorn, and where the young tree had room all its life to throw out its arms as it would ; the little cluster of Birches that springs from the ferns and moss of the hillside. All trees so grown develop an individuality that is not apparent in their fellows of the timber forest ; and however we may delight in the peace and quiet of the forest, with its softened light and cool fragrant air, we can there only regard the trees in a mass.

We might, indeed, reverse the old saying, and declare that we cannot see the trees on account of the wood.

Nature and the timber-producer have different aims and pursue different methods in the making of forests, though the latter is not above taking a hint from the former occasionally. Nature mixes her seeds and sows them broadcast over the land she intends to turn into forest, that the more vigorous kinds may act as nurses, sheltering and protecting the less robust. Then comes the struggle for existence, with its final ending in the survival of the fittest. In the mean time the mixed forest has given shelter to an enormous population of smaller fry—plants, mammals, birds, and insects—and has been a delightful recreation ground for man. The timber-producer aims at so controlling the struggle for existence that the survival of the fit is maintained from start to finish. He plants his young trees in regular order, putting in nurses at intervals and along the borders, intending to cut them down when his purpose has been served. The timber trees are allowed no elbow-room, the putting forth of lateral branches is discouraged, but steady upward growth and the production of "canopy" is abetted. His aim is to get these timber-sticks as near alike as possible, free from individuality, and with the minimum of difference in girth at top and bottom of each pole. This means a thicker and longer balk of clean timber when the tree is felled and squared. The continuous canopy induces growth in the upward direction only, and discourages the weeds and undergrowth that add to the charm of the forest, but which unprofitably use up the wood-producing elements in the soil. This plan contrasts strongly with the views on planting formerly prevalent in this country, John Evelyn, for example, making a special point of giving the Oak room to stretch out its arms, "free from all incumbrances." But, then, unlike the timber-producers, Evelyn had an eye for landscape beauty, and giving an opportunity for the display of such beauty. He says: "And if thus his Majesties forests and chases were stor'd, viz. with this spreading tree at handsom intervals. by which grazing might be improved for the feeding of deer and cattel under them (for such was the old *Saltus*), benignly visited with the gleams of the sun, and adorned with the distant landskips appearing through the glades, and frequent vallies, nothing could be more ravishing."

The greater the success of the forester, the more profound is the solemn stillness of the forest—and the more monotonous. In place of the natural forest, with its varied and teeming life, we have what Wordsworth called a timber factory. In the natural forest, with its mixture of many kinds of trees, the undergrowth of shrubs, and carpet of grass and weeds, the stronger trees spread out their arms in all directions, and fritter away (as the scientific forester would say) their wood-producing powers in making much firewood and little valuable timber. But the result is very beautiful, and the nature-lover can wander among it without tiring, and can study without exhausting its treasures. Emerson says : " In the woods is perpetual youth. Within these plantations of God a decorum and sanctity reign, a perennial festival is dressed, and the guest sees not how he should tire of them in a thousand years." To the scientific forester this is all waste land, and he pleads for the "higher culture" being applied to it. With every desire that the natural resources of our country should be properly developed, we do hope that he will not be entirely successful in his efforts, and that a few of the woods and wastes of Nature's own planting may be left for the recreation of the simple folk who have not yet taken to appraising the value of everything by the price it will fetch in the market.

The trees described in this volume are the really wild growths that have lived a natural life ; and though many of the photographs are from planted trees, they are such as have been allowed to grow as they would, and show the characteristic branching of the species.

A few words on the life of a tree may be welcomed here by those readers who have not made a study of botany. Although the nurseryman makes use of suckers and cuttings for the quicker multiplication of certain species, every tree in its natural habitat produces seeds and is reproduced by them. The flowering of our forest trees is a phenomenon that does not as a rule attract attention, but their fruiting or seed-bearing becomes patent to all who visit the woods in autumn. A tree has lived many years before it is capable of producing seed. The seed-bearing age is different in each species; thus the Oak begins to bear when it is between sixty and seventy years old, the Ash between forty and fifty, the Birch and Sweet Chestnut at twenty-five years. Some produce seed every year after that period is reached, others every second, third, or fifth year; others, again, bear fitfully except at intervals of from six to nine years, when they produce an enormous crop. Most tree-seeds germinate in the spring following their maturity, but they are not all distributed when ripe. The Birch, the Elm, and the Aspen, for examples, disperse their seeds in spring, and these germinate soon after they have been shed.

The seeds contain sufficient nutriment to feed the seedling whilst it is developing its roots and first real leaves. We can, of course, go further back in starting our observations of the life progress of the monarch of the forest. We can dissect the insignificant greenish flower of the Oak when the future seed (acorn) is but a single cell, a tiny bag filled with protoplasm. From that early stage to the period when the tree is first ripe for conversion into timber we span a century and a half, equal to two good human lives, and the Oak is but at the point where a man attains his majority. The Oak is built up after the fashion by which man attains to his full stature. It is a process of multiplication of weak, minute cells, which become specialized for distinct offices in the economy of the vegetable community we call a tree. Some go to renew and enlarge the roots, others to the perfecting of that system of vessels through which the crude fluids from the roots are carried up to the topmost leaf, whence, after undergoing chemical transformation in the leaf laboratory, it is circulated to all parts of the organism to make possible the production of more cells. Each of these has a special task, and it becomes invested with cork or wood to enable it to become part of the bark or the timber; or it remains soft and develops the green colouring matter, which enables it, when exposed to sunlight, to manufacture starch from carbon and water.

This is very similar to what takes place in the human organism, where the nutriment taken in is used up in the production of new cells, which are differentiated into muscle-cells, bone-cells, epidermal-cells, and so forth, building up or renewing muscles or nerves, bones or arteries; but the mechanism of distribution is different, the heart-pump doing the work of capillary attraction and gravitation. The ancients believed in the Dryads, spirits that were imprisoned in trees, and whose life was coterminous with that of the tree; and it will be seen that they had stronger physical justification for their belief than they knew. Shakespeare relates how Sycorax, the witch-mother of Caliban, imprisoned Ariel in a tree; and Huxley finely tells us that " The plant is an animal confined in a wooden case; and Nature, like Sycorax, holds thousands of ' delicate Ariels' imprisoned in every oak. She is jealous of letting us know this; and among the higher and more conspicuous forms of plants reveals it only by such obscure manifestations as the shrinking of the Sensitive Plant, the sudden clasp of the Dionæa, or, still more slightly, by the phenomena of the cyclosis."

The tree, as we have indicated, gets its food from the air and the soil. The rootlets have the power of dissolving the mineral salts in the soil in which they ramify. They are helped materially in this respect—so far as organic matter is concerned, such as the breaking up of dead leaves—by a fungus

that invests them with a mantle of delicate threads known as
Mycorrhiza. So that the fluid that is taken up by the roots
is not merely water, but water plus dissolved mineral matter
and nitrogen. At the same time as the roots are thus absorbing
liquid nutriment, the leaves, pierced with thousands of little
stomata, or mouths, take in atmospheric air, which is com-
pounded chiefly of the gases oxygen and carbon. The leaf-
cells containing the green colouring matter (*chlorophyll*) seize
hold of the carbon and release the oxygen. The carbon is
then combined with the fluid from the roots by the vital
chemistry of the leaves, and is circulated for the sustenance of
all the organs and tissues.

The flowering of the trees varies so greatly that it can only
be dealt with satisfactorily as each species is described. It may
be stated, however, that all the true forest trees are wind-
fertilized, and therefore have inconspicuous greenish blossoms.
By true forest trees we mean those that alone or slightly mixed
are capable of forming high forest. The smaller trees, such as
Crab, Rowan, Cherry, Blackthorn, Hawthorn, Buckthorn, etc.,
belong more to the open woodland, to the common and the
hedgerow. These, from their habitat, can be seen singly, and
therefore can make use of the conspicuous flowers that are
fertilized by insects.

WAYSIDE AND WOODLAND TREES.

---·o·---

PART I.

NATIVE TREES AND SHRUBS.

The Oak (*Quercus robur*).

WHEN good John Evelyn wrote his "Sylva, or a Discourse of Forest Trees," he was greatly concerned lest our "wooden walls" should diminish in strength for want of a succession of stout Oaks in our woodlands, and therefore he put the Oak in the forefront of his discourse. To-day steel and teak have largely supplanted oak in the building of our navy, and our walls of defence are no longer of wood. Yet in spite of these changes, and the consequent reduction of the Oak's importance, we must still look upon it as the typical British tree, and, regardless of its place in botanical classifications, we shall follow the lead of our master and place it first on our list.

There is no necessity for entering upon a minute description of the botanical characters of so well known a tree. The sturdy, massive trunk, firm as a rock; the broad, rounded outline of its head, caused by the downward sweeping extremities of the wide-spreading lower limbs; the wavy outline of the lobed leaves, and the equally distinct egg-and-cup-shaped fruit —these are characters that cannot be confused with those of any other tree, and are the most familiar objects in the landscape in most parts of our islands. To my mind, no wood is so awe-inspiring as one filled with old oaks, all so much alike, yet each with a distinct individuality. We regard with reverence a human centenarian, who may have nothing beyond his great age to commend him to us ; but we think of the long period of history of which he has been a spectator, possibly an active maker of history. The huge Oak has probably lived through ten or twenty such periods. Compared with the Oak, man is but of mushroom growth. It does not produce an acorn until sixty or seventy years old, and even then it is not mature. Not till a century and a half have passed over its head is its timber fit for use, and as a rule it is not felled under the age of two hundred years. Many trees are left to a much greater age, or we should not have still with us so many venerable specimens, and where they have not been left until partially decayed, the timber is found to be still very valuable when finally cut down. Of one of these patriarchs of the forest, cut down in the year 1810, we have figures of quantity and value from a contemporary record. It was known as the Gelenos Oak, and stood about four miles from Newport, Monmouthshire. When felled, it yielded 2426 cubic feet of sound timber, and six tons of bark. It was bought just as it stood for £405, and the purchaser had to pay £82 for labour for stripping, felling, and converting into timber. Five men were employed for twenty days in stripping the bark and felling the tree, and after that a pair of sawyers, working six days a week, were five months cutting it up. But the bark realized £200, and the timber about £400. The timber and bark from this one tree were about equal to the average produce of three acres of oak coppice after fifteen years' growth.

Full-grown oaks vary in height from sixty to one hundred and thirty feet, the difference depending upon situation ; the

Pl. 2.　Oak—summer.　*B* 14.

Oak—winter.

Pl. 3.

tallest, of course, being those that have been drawn up in forests, at the expense of their branches. Trees growing freely in the open are of less height, and are made to appear comparative dwarfs by the huge proportions of the bole. In the forest this may be no more than ten feet in girth, but in

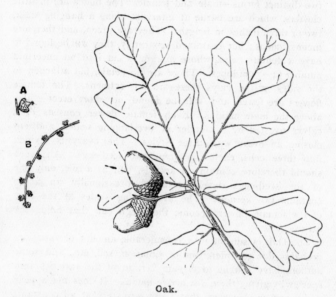

Oak.

A, female flower ; B, male flowers.

isolated specimens may be as much as fifty-four feet (Cowthorpe Oak), with a much broader base. The thick rough bark is deeply furrowed in a large network pattern, which affords temporary hiding-places for insects. The branches are much given to turn and zig-zag from side to side—a character that

C

makes them very useful in boat-building, as "knees" of various angles may be cut from them without having recourse to bending. The best knees are to be obtained from Oaks grown in the hedgerow.

The Oak flowers in April or May, and the blossoms are of two distinct forms—male and female. The males are in little clusters, which are borne at intervals along a hanging stalk, two or three inches in length. They are green, and therefore inconspicuous; but examined separately, they will be found to have a definite calyx, whose margin is cut into an uncertain number (4—7) of lobes. There are no petals, but attached to the sides of the calyx there are ten stamens. The female flowers are fewer, and will be found on short erect stalks above the male catkins. Each female flower consists of a calyx, invested by a number of overlapping scales, and enclosing an ovary with three styles. The ovary is divided into three cells, each containing two seed-eggs. An acorn should therefore contain six kernels, but, as a rule, only one of the seed-eggs develops, though occasionally an acorn contains two kernels. The overlapping scales at the base of the female flower become the rough cup that holds the acorn.

The Oak is subject to a considerable amount of variation, probably due to differences of situation, soil, etc., and some authors have sought to elevate certain of the varieties into species by giving them distinctive names. It does not appear to be certain, however, that these forms are at all constant, and they are connected by intermediate forms that make the identification of many individuals a matter of difficulty. In one of these forms (*sessiliflora*) the stalk of the acorns connecting them with the branch is very short, but the leaves have a distinct footstalk, from half an inch to an inch long. This form is more plentiful in the north and west, and is conspicuous in the Forest of Dean. A second form, known

Pl. 4.

Bole of Oak.

Pl. 5.

Flowers of Oak.

as *pedunculata*, has the leaf-stalk short or absent, the base of the leaf broad and somewhat heart-shaped, and the stalk upon which the acorns are borne very long. A third form (*intermedia*), commonly known as Durmast, has long leaf-stalks, short stalks to the acorns, and the under side of the leaf downy. *Pedunculata* is found more on the lower hills and the sides of valleys, whilst *sessiliflora* prefers higher ground, with a southern or western aspect.

The Oak is most abundant on clay soils, but is at its best when growing in deep sandy loam, where there is also plenty of humus. Its roots in such soil strike down to a depth of five feet, and therefore it thrives in association with Beech, whose roots are much nearer the surface, and whose fallen leaves supply it with humus.

The Oak is more persistently attacked by insects than any other tree. One authority (Leunis) has tabulated the species that get their living mainly or entirely from their attacks on the foliage, timber, or bark, and they number about five hundred. With some species this warfare is waged on so extensive a scale, that in some years by early summer the Oaks are almost divested of their foliage, and a new crop of leaves becomes a necessity. But the reserve forces of the Oak are quite equal to this drain, and the tree does not appear to suffer, though a much less thorough attack would be serious to a Conifer. One of the worst of these Oak-spoilers —though it by no means restricts its energies to attacks on this tree—is the Mottled Umber Moth (*Hibernia defoliaria*), whose pretty caterpillars may be seen hanging by silken threads from the leafless twigs.

A striking Oak insect is the Stag Beetle (*Lucanus cervus*), which, in warm evenings in the south of England, may be seen flying round the Oaks, the size and antler-like jaws of the male arousing feelings of respect in the minds of those who are not acquainted with its habits. The formidable-looking "horns" are usually harmless. The beetle spends its larval stage in the wood of unhealthy Oaks, and, when mature, seeks his hornless mate among its foliage.

Perhaps the most interesting of the Oak's pensioners to the woodland rambler will be the varied forms of gall on different parts of the tree. There is the so-called Oak-apple, of uneven surface and spongy to the touch, which certain people still wear on May 29th, in honour of Charles II. ; the well-rounded hard Bullet-gall of *Cynips kollari*, the Artichoke-gall of *Cynips gemmæ*, the Spangle-galls of *Neuroterus lenticularis*, so plentiful on the back of the leaf, and the Root-gall of *Biorhiza aptera*. All these galls are abnormal growths, due to the irritation set up by the Gall-wasps named, when they pierced the young tissues in order to lay their eggs in them. Where any of these galls are perforated it may be known that the Gall-wasp whose grub fed within has flown, but where there is no such perforation the grub is still within, feeding upon the flesh of the gall, or in the chrysalis stage, awaiting translation to the winged condition.

Several Oaks of foreign origin are also grown in our parks and open spaces ; among them the Holm Oak (*Quercus ilex*) whose evergreen leathery leaves have toothed or plain edges, and occasionally the lower ones develop marginal spines, whence its name of Holm or Holly Oak. It is notable for retaining its lower branches, so that its appearance, as Loudon remarks, "even when fully grown, is that of an immense bush, rather than that of a timber tree." It is a native of Southern Europe and North Africa, and appears to have been introduced about the middle of the sixteenth century. It usually attains a height of from twenty to thirty feet, but occasionally specimens are seen up to sixty feet. It has a much thinner, more even bark than that of our native Oak, and of a black colour. The long brown acorns do not ripen until the second year.

Pl. 6.

Holm Oak.

Acorns of Turkey Oak.

Pl. 7.

Fruit of Beech.

Pl. 8.

Pl. 9.

Beech—summer.

The Turkey Oak (*Quercus cerris*) is a much larger tree, attaining to similar heights to our British Oak, but easily distinguishable by its more pyramidal outline, and its attenuated leaves. The lance-shaped lobes of these are unequal, sharp, and angular; and the footless acorn-cups are covered with bristly or mossy-looking scales. The acorns, which are small and exceedingly bitter, rarely ripen till their second autumn. The whole tree—trunk, branches, and twigs—is of straighter growth than *Quercus robur*. It is a native of Southern Europe and the Levant, and was introduced about the year 1735.

The spring rambler in the woods may come upon a party of woodmen stripping young Oaks of their bark, or felling them, whilst cylinders of separated bark rest across poles in the process of drying. This is the industry of barking for the purpose of the tanner. When the Oaks in a coppice are about sixteen years old they are most suitable for this purpose, the bark then containing a larger percentage of *tannin* than at other period. The operation is best performed in May, when the sap is in flow, and should be completed between the first swelling of the leaf-buds and the unrolling of the leaves. If the weather is cold and damp the bark will peel the better, provided there is an absence of north or east winds. Before the tree is cut down the bole is stripped, the first ring being taken from just above the roots to a height of two and a half feet above. When the tree is felled, it is cut into lengths and the bark stripped from them; then all branches that are an inch or more in diameter are peeled. The bark is piled to dry for a couple of weeks, and is then broken into small pieces and sent away in sacks.

It is not alone in the use of the bark that the tannic acid of the Oak is made evident; it is to the presence of this that the austerity of the acorn is due, and also the ink-producing properties of certain Oak-galls. Everything connected with the tree gets a roughness of flavour from this same principle. Even that remarkable fungus, the Vegetable Beef-steak, that may be found on old Oaks in autumn, is impregnated with it.

Prior regards the name Oak (Anglo-Saxon *ac*) as originally belonging to the fruit, and only later transferred to the tree that produces it. The more obvious explanation (though we know that in etymological and other matters the obvious is not always the true interpretation) is, that acorn (ac-corn) signified the corn or fruit of the ac. Selby tells us that "During the Anglo-Saxon rule, and even for some time after the Conquest, Oak-forests were chiefly valued for the fattening of swine. Laws relating to pannage, or the fattening of hogs in the forest, were enacted during the Heptarchy; and by Ina's statutes, any person wantonly injuring or destroying an Oak-tree was mulcted in a fine varying according to size, or the quantity of mast it produced."

The Beech (*Fagus sylvatica*).

We speak of the Oak as the "Monarch of the Woods," and to the Beech the title "Mother of Forests" has been given. To the timber-merchant the Beech has little importance, but the grower of timber freely acknowledges his heavy indebtedness to this nursing mother, for, in the words of Professor Gayer, the Bavarian forestry expert, "without Beech there can no more be properly tended forests of broad-leaved genera, as along with it would have to be given up many other valuable timber-trees, whose production is only possible with the aid of Beech." Quite apart from utilitarian considerations, we should be very sorry to lose the Beech, with its towering, massive shaft clad in smooth grey bark, its spreading roots above the soil, and the dense shade of its fine foliage. Fortunately for the lover of natural beauty, it is this luxuriant growth of leaves and the shade it gives that are the redeeming virtues of the Beech

Pl. 10.

Acorns of Pedunculate Oak.

Pl. II.

C 21.

Bole of Beech.

in the eye of the forester. Its drip destroys most of the soil-exhausting weeds, its shade protects the soil from over-evaporation, and the heavy crop of leaves enriches it by their decomposition. On these points the forestry experts of to-day join hands with John Evelyn, who, nearly 250 years ago, thus referred to it—"The shade unpropitious to corn and grass, but sweet, and of all the rest, most refreshing to the weary shepherd—*lentus in umbra*, echoing Amaryllis with his oaten pipe." And, again, after giving us a long catalogue of the varied uses to which Beechwood may be put, he adds—"Yet for all this, you would not wonder to hear me deplore the so frequent use of this wood, if you did consider that the industry of France furnishes that country for all domestic utensils with excellent Walnut, a material infinitely preferable to the best Beech, which is indeed good only for shade and for the fire." In the days of open hearths and chimney corners the Beech was extensively used for fuel, and it is still reputed to make good charcoal; but to-day the chairmaker and the turner are the chief users of its wood.

The Beech well grown attains a height of about 100 feet, and a girth of 20 feet. There was, until recently, a Beech in Norbury Park, Surrey, 160 feet in height. Its branches horizontally spreading gave it a head of enormous proportions. Hooker gives the *diameter* of the Knowle Beech as 352 feet, which means a circumference of about as many yards. It will grow in most upland places where the Oak thrives, though it does not need so deep a soil, and has a preference for land containing lime. Fresh mineral soils, rich in humus, are the best for it. In poor soils its growth is slow and its life is longer. It begins to bear mostly at about eighteen years of age, and thereafter gives good crops at intervals of three or five years.

In spring, just before the buds expand, the twigs of the Beech have a very distinct appearance. They are long and slender, placed alternately along the twig, and the brown envelopes retain their shape long after they have been cast off. It is interesting to note how well these are mimicked by a glossy spindle-shaped snail (*Clausilia laminata*) that has a decided fondness for the Beech. As the snails crawl up the bole or over the moss at its base, it is not easy at a glance to say which are snails and which bud-envelopes. This is one of the protective resemblances adopted by many animals to give them a chance of eluding their natural enemies—in this case the thrush and other birds.

In the bud the leaf is folded fan-wise, and the folds run parallel with the nerves. They expand into an oval, smooth-faced leaf, with slightly scooped edges, and a most delicate fringe of short gossamer, which falls off later. These leaves Evelyn recommended as a stuffing for beds, declaring that if " gathered about the fall, and somewhat before they are much frost-bitten, [they] afford the best and easiest mattresses in the world to lay under our quilts instead of straw. . . . In Switzerland I have sometimes lain on them to my great refreshment." That last clause seems to imply that the authorities at home would not allow the introduction of new-fangled bed-stuffings, but remained true to straw. These leaves are rich in potash, and as they readily decay, they produce an admirable humus. In sheltered places the leaves, turned to a light ruddy-brown colour, are retained on the lower branches until cast off by the expansion of the new buds.

In early summer, whilst the leaves are still pellucid, the shade of a big Beech is particularly inviting. Later the leaves become opaque, and their glossy surfaces throw back the heat rays. Then the play of light upon the great mass of foliage is very fine ; but when autumn has turned their deep green to orange and warm ruddy brown, and they catch the red rays of the westering sun, the tree appears to be turned into a blazing fire.

The Beech flowers in April or May. The blossoms are rather more conspicuous than is the case with the Oak, for the male

Pl. 12.

Beech—winter.

Pl. 13.

Birch—summer.

flowers are gathered together in a hanging purplish-brown
rounded tassel with yellow anthers. The female flowers, to the
number of two, three, or four, are clustered in a "cupule" of
overlapping scales, like those of the Oak. But in the Beech the
"cupule" becomes a bristly closed box, which afterwards opens

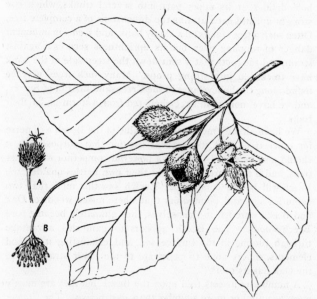

Leaves, flowers, and fruit of Beech.
A, female ; B, male flowers.

by one end splitting into four triangular silk-hair-lined valves,
which turn back and reveal the three-sided, sharp-edged "mast."
This mast was formerly a very valuable product of the Beech-
woods, when herds of swine were turned in them to feed upon
the fallen Beech-nuts. Agricultural methods have changed ;

D

but though our hogs are now confined in styes, and fed on a
diet that more rapidly fattens, Beech-mast is still a good food
eagerly taken by such woodland denizens as badgers, deer,
squirrels, and dormice.

The vitality of the Beech is so high that quite frequently the
bole divides at its upper part into several trunks, which rise
straight up, and each attains the dimensions of a complete tree.
Often such a tree stands on a sandy bank, and seems in imminent
danger of toppling over, but its uprightness secures it against
strain, and the roots that it sent down the steep side of the bank
have thickened into strong props. Many such trees may be
found along the hollow lanes in the Greensand district of Surrey,
and we have more than once sheltered from a storm under their
roots.

We have already mentioned the value of the Beech as a nurse
for other trees, and its frequent use for that purpose, but it
should also be stated that it is a powerful competitor with other
trees, and if these are left to fight their own battles unaided, the
Beech will be the conqueror. Evelyn saw this more than two
centuries ago, and pointed out that where mixed woods of Oak
and Beech were left to themselves, they ultimately became pure
Beech-woods. The Beech appears to gain this advantage
through rooting in the surface soil, and, exhausting it of food
elements, suffers none to penetrate to the lower strata, where
the Oak has its roots.

A number of insects feed upon the Beech, but they are mostly
more beautiful or more singular than destructive. The Copper
Beech, which is so effectively used for ornament in parks, is
merely a sub-variety of the Common Beech, and all the examples
in cultivation are believed to be "sports" from the purple
variety, which itself was a natural sport discovered in a German
wood little more than a hundred years ago.

The modern word Beech is derived from the Anglo-Saxon
boc, bece, beoce, which had very similar equivalents in all branches

Pl. 14.

Bole of Birch.

Catkins of Birch.

of the German and Scandinavian family, and from the fact that
the literature of these people was inscribed on tablets of Beech,
our word *book* has the same origin.

The Birch (*Betula alba*).

" The Lady of the Woods," as Coleridge christened the Birch,
is at once the most graceful, the hardiest, and the most ubiqui-
tous of our forest trees. It grows throughout the length and
breadth of our islands, and seems happy alike on a London
common, in a suburban garden, or far up in the Scottish highlands (2500 feet). It penetrates farther north than any other
tree, and its presence is a great boon to the natives of Lapland.
It will grow where it is subjected to great heat, as well as where
it must endure extreme cold, with its slender roots exploring
the beds of peat, the rich humus of the old wood, or the raw
soil of the mountain-side, where it has to cling to rocks and a
few mosses. Given plenty of light, and it seems to care for
little else. Though a mere shrub in the far north, with us the
Birch has a trunk sometimes as tall as eighty, but more frequently fifty feet, and a girth of from two to three feet. In its
first decade it increases in height at the rate of a foot and a
half or two feet in a year ; but, of course, there is little breadth
to be built up at the same time. It reaches maturity in half a
century, and before the other half is reached the Birch will have
passed away.

The bark of the Birch is more enduring than its timber,
which may be partly due to its habit of casting off the outer
layer in shreds, like fine tissue-paper, from time to time. The
greater part of the bark is silvery white, which adds to the
apparent slenderness of the tree, and makes it conspicuous from
a long distance ; for the attenuated and drooping branches,
dressed in small and loosely hung leaves, sway so constantly

that the trunk is scarcely hidden. The glossy, leathery leaves vary in shape from a triangular form to a pointed oval, their edges doubly toothed, and their footstalks long and slender.

About April the hanging catkins of the Birch, which were in evidence in the previous autumn, have matured and become dark crimson ; the scales separate and expose the two stamens of each flower, which has a single sepal. The female flowers are in a short, more erect spike, which consists of overlapping scales (*bracts*), each containing two or three flowers. The flowers have neither petals nor sepals, each consisting merely of an ovary with two slender styles. After fertilization the female spike has developed into a little oblong cone. The minute nuts have a pair of delicate wings to each, and as they are set free from the cones they flutter on the breeze like a swarm of small flies. The moss that usually covers the ground beneath the Birch will be found in October to be thickly speckled with these fruits, which are something more than seeds, as they are commonly termed ; they are really analogous to the acorn —a nut within a thin shell. The tree sometimes begins to produce seed when only fifteen years old ; but, as a rule, it is ten years older before it bears, and thereafter it has a crop every year.

It is strange how so striking and graceful a tree could have been so persistently ignored by the old school of landscape painters, when one remembers with what good effect modern artists have utilized it. In this connection we need not apologize for quoting at length a description of the tree from the artist's point of view, because it also gives attention to those points one would like the rambler to notice. Mr. P. G. Hamerton in his *Sylvan Year*, says—

"The stem . . . of the Silver Birch is one of the masterpieces of Nature. Everything has been done to heighten its unrivalled brilliance. The horizontal peeling of the bark, making dark rings at irregular distances, the brown spots, the dark colour of the small twigs, the rough texture near the ground, and the exquisite silky smoothness of the tight white bands above, offer exactly that variety of contrast which makes us feel a rare quality like that smooth whiteness as strongly as we are capable of feeling it. And amongst the common effects in all northern

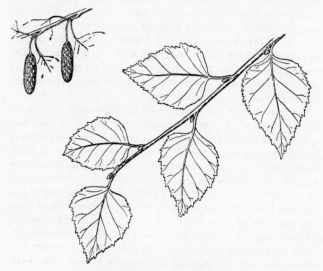

Birch leaves and catkins.

countries, one of the most brilliant is the opposition of birch trunks in sunshine against the deep blue or purple of a mountain distance in shadow. At all seasons of the year the beauty of the birch is attractive and peculiarly its own. The young beech may remind you of it occasionally under strong effects of light, and is also very graceful, but we have no tree that rivals the

birch in its own qualities of colour and form, still less in that
air and bearing which are so much more difficult to describe.
In winter you see the full delicacy of the sprays that the lightest
foliage hides, and in early spring this tree clothes itself, next
after the willow, with tiny triangular leaves, inexpressibly light
in the mass, so that from a distance they have the effect of a
green mist rather than anything more material. When the
tree is isolated sufficiently to come against the sky, you may
see one of the prettiest sights in Nature—the pure deep azure
of heaven, with the silvery white and fresh green of the birch in
opposition. And yet it is not a crude green, for there is a good
deal of warm red in it, which gives one of those precious ter-
tiaries that all true colourists value."

Linnæus named our common Birch *Betula alba;* but more
than a century ago Ehrhart pointed out that there were two
well-defined forms of the tree, which he proposed to separate as
distinct species under the names of *B. verrucosa* and *B. pubescens.* Hooker regards the first of these as the typical form, for
which he properly retains the Linnean name. It is distinguished
by having the base of the bole covered with coarse, rough, and
blackish bark, the *smooth* leaves looking as though their base
had been cut off, and the twigs warty. The *B. pubescens* of
Ehrhart appears to be a variety of Fries' *B. glutinosa,* which
Hooker treats as a sub-species of *B. alba.* Roth, however, had
named this form *B. pendula* a few years earlier. The bark
at its base is smooth and white, its *downy* leaves have a
triangular base, and its twigs are free from warts.

The Dwarf Birch (*Betula nana*) is a distinct species, which
occurs locally in the mountainous parts of Northumberland and
Scotland. It is not a tree, but a bush, only two or three feet in
height. Its firm-textured, round leaves have scalloped margins
and short footstalks.

The foliage of the Birch in autumn turns to a yellow hue. At
this period—and, indeed, for a month earlier—there may be

Pl. 16.

Birch—winter.

Pl. 17.

D 29.

Alder—summer.

seen beneath the Birch-trees one of the most striking of our toadstools, the Fly Agaric (*Amanita muscarius*), so-called from its use as the lethal ingredient in the making of fly-papers. From a bulbous base a creamy yellow stem arises, decked about half its height with an ample hanging frill. The upper side of the spreading "cap" is painted with crimson, over which are scattered flecks of white or cream kid—the remains of an outer envelope that was ruptured by the expansion of the cap, and of which the frill represents the lower portion. This species is really poisonous, and the Kamschatkans are said to make their *vodka* superlatively intoxicating by the addition of this fungus to it. On the trunk of the Birch may sometimes be found a large fungus named *Polyporus betulinus*, whose root-like portion penetrates the bark and sucks up the sap.

Birch-bark is used for tanning certain kinds of leather, and the peculiar odour of Russian leather is said to be due to the use of Birch in its preparation. The Birch agrees with the Beech in two respects—it is of little value for timber, but as a nurse to young timber-trees it is of considerable importance. Its name is from the Anglo-Saxon *beorc*, *birce*, and signifies the Bark-tree.

The Alder (*Alnus rotundifolia*).

Although the Alder is abundant by riversides and in all low-lying moist lands as far north as Caithness, it is not so generally well known at sight as the Oak, the Beech, and the Birch. It is a small tree, ordinarily only thirty to forty feet in height, with a girth from three to six feet, though occasionally it aspires to seventy feet in height. This is when it is growing in moist loam, upon which rain or floods have washed down good layers of humus from woods at a higher elevation. If, with its roots thus well cared for, its head is in a humid atmosphere, the Alder is in happy case. If it has had the misfortune to get into a porous soil, though this may be moist enough to please an Ash, the Alder becomes merely a big bush.

The bark of the Alder is rough and black, and the wood soft. Whilst the tree is alive its wood is white, but when cut and exposed to the air it becomes red ; finally, on drying, it changes to

Alder.

a pinkish tint. As timber it has no great reputation, except for piles or other submerged purposes, when it is said to be exceedingly durable. It has also enjoyed a great reputation for making the best charcoal for the gunpowder mills, and it is largely used by the turner, the wood-carver, and the cabinet-

Pl. 18.

Catkins of Alder.

Pl. 19.

Bole of Alder.

maker. The leaves, which have short stalks, and are from two to four inches long, are roundish with a wedge-shaped base. They have a waved and toothed margin, and remain green long after the leaves of other trees have fallen. In their young condition these leaves are covered with hairs, and are sticky to the touch, and when older they retain a distinct suggestion of greasiness. There are bacteria nodules on the roots.

The flowering of the Alder is very similar to that of the Birch, but the male catkins have red scales, and each flower four stamens. The female spikes have the fleshy scales covered by red-brown bracts of a woody consistence, which persist after the fruit has dropped out of them. Seed is not produced until the Alder is twenty years old, and the crop is repeated almost every year after. The cones are ripe about October or November, when they scatter their fruit, but the empty ones persist in hanging to the branches throughout the winter in numbers sufficient to give the leafless tree a brown appearance from a little distance. The immature male catkins are in evidence at the same time.

There is a variety (*incisa*) of the Alder in which the leaves are so deeply toothed that they bear a close resemblance to those of the Hawthorn.

In some localities the tree is called the Howler and Aller, the latter word apparently the original name, for its Anglo-Saxon forms were *ælr*, *alr*, and *aler*.

The Hornbeam (*Carpinus betulus*).

The Hornbeam is frequently passed by as a Beech, to which it has a very close superficial likeness, but a comparison of leaves, flowers, or bole would at once make the differences obvious. It is usually found in similar situations to the Beech, though it does not ascend so far up the hills as that species. On dry, poor soils it does not attain its full proportions and may only be classed as a small tree; but when growing on low ground, in rich loam

E

or good clay, it reaches a height of seventy feet, with a girth of ten feet. If two measurements of the bole's diameter be taken at right angles to each other, they will be found to differ greatly. A section of the trunk will not show a circular outline, but rather an ellipse, the bole appearing to have been flattened on two sides. It is coated with a smooth grey bark, usually spotted with white.

The leaves are less symmetrical than those of Beech, and are broader towards the base. They are of rougher texture, hairy on the underside, and their edges are doubly toothed. In autumn they turn yellow, then to ruddy gold, but a few days later they have settled into the rusty hue they retain throughout the winter, in those cases where they remain on the tree until spring.

The wood is exceedingly tough, and not to be worked up with ease, but it is considered to make admirable fuel. Evelyn says, " It burns like a candle." There are those who say that the name Hornbeam has reference to the tough or hornlike character of its beams; others declare that in the days when bullocks were yoked to the plough the yoke was made of this wood, as being fitted by its toughness to stand the strain, and as it was attached to the horns it became the horn-beam. A third theory is that the name was derived from *Ornus*, the Manna-ash, with which early botanists confused it, but with all respect to the authority of Dr. Prior, who favours it, we prefer to stand on the first suggestion, with old John Gerarde, who says ("Herball," 1633): " In time it waxeth so hard that the toughnesse and hardnesse of it may be rather compared to horn than unto wood, and therefore it was called Hornbeam or hardbeam." The carpenter is not pleased who has hornbeam to work up, for his tools lose their edge far too quickly for his labour to be profitable. Evelyn tells us that it was called by some the Horse-beech, from the resemblance of the leaves.

The two kinds of catkins are similar and cylindrical, but whilst the male is pendulous from the beginning, the female is

Pl. 20.

Alder—winter.

Pl. 21.

Hornbeam—summer.

erect until after the formation of the fruit, when it gradually
assumes the hanging position. The bracts of the male are oval,
with sharp tips, each containing an uncertain (3–12) number of
stamens.   In the female the bracts fall early, but their place
is taken by three-lobed bracteoles, which enlarge after flowering

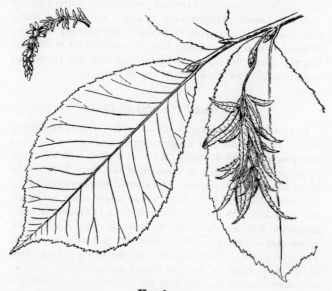

Hornbeam.

and become an inch or an inch and a half long. A single flower
occupies each bracteole, consisting of a two-celled ovary and two
styles.   Only one cell develops, so that the hard green fruit contains but one seed.   The appearance of these fruits in autumn
as they hang in a spray from the underside of the branches **is**
quite distinct from those of any other of our native trees.

The Hornbeam's title to be considered indigenous has had some doubts thrown upon it because there are some records of specimens having been introduced during the fifteenth century, but that is not sufficient ground upon which to deny nationality. We have known persons to bring home from distant parts as treasures wild plants and ferns that were growing within a mile of their own homes. It appears to be a real native of the south-east and midland counties of England, and possibly of Wales. A line drawn across the map from Worcestershire to Norfolk roughly marks the limit ; north of that line the Hornbeam appears to have been planted, as also in Ireland.

The Hazel (*Corylus avellana*).

It is rarely that the Hazel is allowed in this country to develop into a tree ; as a rule it is a shrub, forming undergrowth in wood or copse, or part of a hedge. As it is cut down with the copse or hedge, it cannot form a standard of any size. But that the Hazel left alone will develop into a small tree is shown by an example in Eastwell Park, Kent, whose height a few years ago was thirty feet, with a circumference of three feet round the bole. As soon as the nuts are formed the bush is easily identified by all, so that a description of its character is hardly necessary. The large, roundish, heart-shaped leaves are arranged alternately in two rows along the straight downy shoots. Their margins are doubly toothed, and when in the bud they are plaited, the folds being parallel to the midrib. Soon after the buds open, many of the leaves assume a purplish tint for a while ; in autumn they turn brown, and finally pale to yellow.

Before the leaves appear the Hazel is rendered conspicuous by the male catkins, which are familiar to country children under the name of Lamb's-tails. These may be seen in an undeveloped condition in the autumn, when the nuts are being sought. A cluster of two or three hard, little, grey-green cylinders is all that may

Pl. 22.

Hornbeam—winter.

Pl. 23.

Bole of Hornbeam.

Pl. 24.

Fruits of Hornbeam.

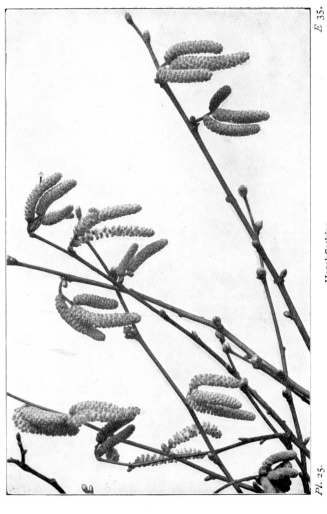

Hazel Catkins.

Pl. 25.

then be seen of them ; but throughout the winter they lengthen, their scales loosen, and in February they are a couple of inches long, pliant, and yellow with the abundant pollen which blows out of them as they swing. The female flowers are by no means conspicuous, and have to be looked for. They will be found in the

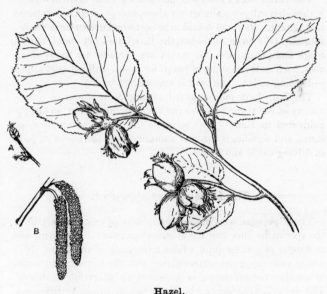

Hazel.

A. female flowers ; B, male flowers.

form of swollen buds on the upper parts of the shoots and branches, from which issue some fine crimson threads. These are the styles and stigmas, and on dissection of the budlike head, each pair of styles will be seen to spring from a two-celled ovary nestling between the bracts or scales of which the head is composed. It is only rarely that the seed-egg in each cell develops ; as a rule one shrivels, and the other develops into the sweet " kernel " of the Hazel-nut.   The shell is the ovary that has become woody and hard ; the ragged-edged leathery " shuck " is the enlarged bracts that surrounded the minute flower.

The Hazel likes a good soil, and will not really flourish without it, though it will *grow* almost anywhere, except where the moisture is stagnant.   Its wood is said to be best when grown on a chalky subsoil.   Of course, as timber, the Hazel does not count, but its tough and pliant rods and staves are valuable for many small uses, such as the making of hoops for casks, walking-sticks, and —divining-rods !   The bark is smooth and brown.

The Barcelona nut, imported so largely in winter, is only a variety of the Hazel ; as also the Cob and the Filbert, so largely cultivated in Kent.   The name is the Anglo-Saxon *hœsl*, or *hœsel*, and signifies a baton of authority, from the use of its rods in driving cattle and slaves.

The Lime (*Tilia platyphyllos*).

Those persons who obtain their ideas of trees mainly from the specimens they can see in suburban roads and gardens are in danger of getting quite a false impression of the Lime.   It is a long suffering, good-tempered tree, and like human individuals of similar temperament, is subjected to shameful treatment. The suburban gardener who has a row of Limes to trim uses the saw, and amputates every arm close up to the shoulder, so that when the season of budding and burgeoning arrives the row of Limes will look like an upward extension in green of the brick wall.   Such are the atrocities upon which Suburbia has to base its ideas of one of the most imposing of trees.

The Large-leaved Lime, growing in park-land or meadow, with its roots deep in good light loam, and its head eighty or

Pl. 26.

Hazel Nuts.

Pl. 27.

Lime-tree—summer.

ninety feet above, is quite another matter. Such a tree is a thing of beauty, and one can stand long at its base looking up among the wide-spreading limbs so well clothed with leaves of fine texture and tint. The girth of such a specimen at four feet from the ground would be about fifteen feet. Larger individuals have been recorded, up to twenty-seven feet.

There are three kinds of Lime in general cultivation in this country, but the differences between them are not great. They are the Large-leaved (*Tilia platyphyllos*), the Small-leaved (*T. parvifolia*), and the Intermediate or Common Lime (*T. europæa*). The last-named is generally admitted to be an introduced kind, and it is the one most commonly planted. Respecting the claims of the other two to rank as natives, there has been some difference of opinion among authorities. The Small-leaved Lime, which does not occur in woods north of Cumberland, was regarded by Borrer as a true indigene, but H. C. Watson considered its claims as open to doubt, though he had no such doubt of the Large-leaved Lime, which is only growing really wild in the woods of Herefordshire, Radnorshire, and the West Riding of Yorkshire.

All our Limes have similar straight tall stems, clad in smooth bark, and with a similar habit of growth. They are trees that demand genial climatic conditions for their proper development, and in consequence they do not put forth their leaves until May. The period of their leafy glory is comparatively short, for they are among the trees that lose their leaves earliest in autumn, after having been for a few days transmuted into gold. The leaf of the Lime is heart-shaped, with one of the basal lobes larger than the other, and the edges cut into saw-like teeth. There are slight differences in those of the three species, which will be indicated below.

In its floral arrangements the Lime differs from the trees previously mentioned in that it has distinct sepals and petals, an abundance of honey, and strong, sweet fragrance as of

Honeysuckle. Unlike them, it does not trust to so rough and ready an agent of fertilization as the wind, so that it waits until its boughs are well clothed with leaves before putting forth its yellowish-white blossoms. These are in clusters (*cymes*) of six or seven, the stalks of all arising from one very long and stouter stalk, which is attached for half its length to a thin and narrow

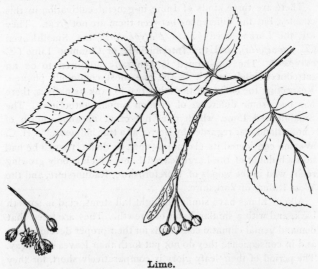

Lime.

bract. Individually regarded, the flowers will be found to consist of five sepals, five petals, an oval ovary with a style ending in a five-toothed stigma, and surrounded by a large number of stamens. The stamens discharge their pollen before the stigma of that flower is fitted to receive it, so that cross-fertilization is ensured by the visits of the innumerable bees that visit the flowers for the abundant nectar they contain, and which the bees convert into a first-rate honey.

Flowers of Lime.

Pl. 28.

Fruits of Lime.

Pl. 29.

Pl. 30.

Bole of Lime.

Pl. 31

Lime—winter.

The flowers are succeeded by globose little fruits, each about a quarter of an inch across, yellow, and covered with pale down. In a good season these will be found to contain one or two seeds, but too often in this country the summers are too cool to ripen them. The Lime does not begin to bear until about its thirty-fifth year. It flowers every year thereafter, but the question of its seed-crop depends entirely upon the weather.

For the purposes to which large timber is usually put, the light white wood of the Lime is not highly esteemed, not being considered of sufficient durability; yet it serves for many smaller uses, where its lightness and fine grain are strong recommendations. It must not be forgotten that the wonderful carvings of Grinling Gibbons were executed in this wood. It is largely used by the makers of musical instruments; and, as every one knows, it is from the inner bark of the Lime that those useful bast mats, which are imported from Russia in such large numbers, are made. Probably owing to its lightness, again, the wood was used in old times for making bucklers. The question of its value as timber is probably never taken into account when it is planted in this country, where its ornamental appearance as an avenue or shade-tree is its great recommendation. It is one of the long-lived trees, its full life-period being certainly five centuries. Those in St. James's Park are popularly supposed to have been planted, at the suggestion of John Evelyn, some-where about the year 1660. There is a fine Lime avenue in Bushey Park, probably planted by Dutch William.

Deer and cattle are fond of the foliage and young shoots if they can get at them. Numerous insects exhibit a like partiality; of these the caterpillar of the large and hand-some Lime Hawk-moth (*Smerinthus tiliæ*) is the most characteristic.

The differences between the three species may be briefly noted :—

SMALL-LEAVED LIME (*Tilia parvifolia*). Does not attain the large proportions of the others. Leaves about two inches across, smooth ; on the lower surface the axils of the nerves are glaucous and downy, with hairy patches between nerves. Fruit thin-shelled and brittle, downy, and very faintly ribbed. The upper leaves show a tendency to lobing.

LARGE-LEAVED LIME (*Tilia platyphyllos*). Bark rougher. Twigs hairy. Leaves larger (four inches) and rougher, downy beneath, axils of the nerves woolly. Fruit of more oval shape, woody and strongly ribbed when ripe.

COMMON LIME (*Tilia europæa*). Intermediate between the others. Leaves larger than those of *T. parvifolia*, smaller than those of *T. platyphyllos;* downy in axils beneath. Twigs smooth. Fruit woody, but without ribs.

The name Lime was originally Linde, a form which, with the addition of *n*, is in use to-day. Chaucer and other English writers spell it Line and Lyne, and the transition from this form to that commonly used to-day 'has been effected by changing the *n* to *m*. Originally it meant *pliant*, and had reference to the useful bast from which cordage and other flexible things were made.

Wych Elm (*Ulmus*).

There are three kinds of Elms commonly met with in England, and of these two are known as Wych Elm. These we may call the Rough-leaved Wych Elm (*Ulmus scabra*) and the Smooth-leaved Wych Elm (*U. glabra*). The Small-leaved, Common or English Elm (*U. campestris*), so freely planted in the hedgerows of Southern England, is the third kind ; and in addition there are local varieties and hybrids, such as the Cornish Elm, the Huntingdon Elm, and the Jersey Elm. Until quite recently it had been accepted generally that the Common Elm had been introduced by the Romans ; but it proves to be unknown anywhere as a wild tree. Mr.

Pl. 32.

Wych Elm—summer.

Fruits of Wych Elm.

Pl. 33.

Augustine Henry has lately demonstrated the probability that it is really English, as one of its names indicates ; that it is descended from a crossing of the two species of Wych Elms. Wych Elms are also known as Mountain Elm, Scots Elm, and Witch Hazel, under the Latin name *montana*.

The philologists appear to be uncertain as to the origin and meaning of Wych, but it seems most probably a form of Witch. Just as a Hazel-rod is used by water-finders, who declare that its movements indicate the presence of hidden springs, so a wand of Elm may have furnished the witch-finder with a Witch-Hazel for the detection of witches !

Although the Rough-leaved Elm is found at an elevation of 1300 feet in Yorkshire, and the Common Elm at 1500 feet in Derbyshire, they are distinctly trees of lowlands and valleys.

The Wych Elm forms a trunk of large size, from 80 to 120 feet or more in height, with a girth of 50 feet, and covered with rough bark that is often corky. Its long slender branches spread widely with a downward tendency, the downy forking twigs bearing their leaves in a straight row along each side. The leaves are somewhat oval in general form, but the two sides of the midrib are unequal in size and shape. Their edges are doubly or trebly toothed, and the surfaces are rough and harsh to the touch. The hairs that cover the strong ribs on the under surface serve for the protection of the breathing pores from dust. On leaves of the pendulous form of this tree, grown in the London parks and gardens, these hairs will be found to be quite black with the soot particles gathered from the air. Trees need carbon, but in this gross form they are too often suffocated by it.

In Feb. or March the brownish flowers are produced in bunches from the sides of the branches. They are a quarter of an inch long, bell-shaped, their edges cut into lobes, and finely fringed. The ovary, with its two awl-shaped styles, is surrounded by four or five stamens with purple anthers. They appear in Feb. or March, before the leaf-buds have opened, and are dependent on the wind for the transfer of pollen. The fruit is an oblong *samara*, about an inch long. This consists of a single seed in the centre, invested by a thin envelope, which is extended all round as a light membranous wing, which gives it buoyancy and enables it to float through the air to a little

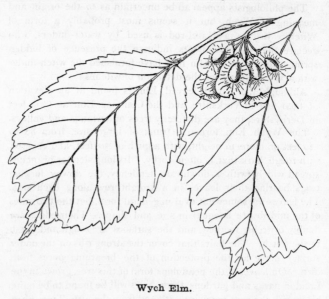

Wych Elm.

distance. These seeds are not produced until about the thirtieth year of the tree's life, and though they are ripened almost annually thereafter, good crops are biennial or triennial only. It has often been stated that the Wych Elm does not send up suckers, but the Smooth-leaved form does—chiefly as the result of root-pruning or some other check to the extension of the root-system.

Pl. 34.

Bole of Wych Elm.

Pl. 35.

Wych Elm—winter.

Pl. 36.

Common Elm—summer.

Pl. 37.

Bole of Common Elm.

The Elm most frequently seen is the Small-leaved Elm (*Ulmus campestris*), which is therefore entitled to its alternative name of Common Elm. Constantly grown as a hedgerow tree, it meets us at every turn, though it is much less plentiful in Scotland than in other parts of the United Kingdom. It is in all respects very similar to the Wych Elm, but its leaves are smaller—usually from two to three inches long, the twigs often covered with a corky bark, and the seed, instead of being in the centre of the samara, is much nearer to the notched end. The leaves are proportionately narrower than those of *scabra*, and it will be found that the hairs which cover the midrib below possess in minor degree the irritating qualities of the Nettle's stings. This is a fact not generally known, but I became painfully aware of it a few years ago when clearing away the suckers of an Elm that were encroaching too much upon my garden border. Examination of these hairs shows that they are constructed much on the same plan as those of the Nettle—a member of the same Natural Order, by the way. The fact that these leaves are browsed by cattle and deer may explain this development of the hairs, which, whilst they may serve to keep off sheep, have not yet reached a degree of acridity sufficient to protect them from the larger beasts. Both flowers and samaras are about a third smaller than those of *scabra;* but fertile seed is very seldom produced, and the tree seeks to reproduce itself by throwing up abundant suckers round the base of the bole, and even from root-branches at a considerable distance from the trunk. These, of course, if allowed to grow, would soon surround the tree with copse.

Campestris often attains a greater height with its straighter trunk than *scabra*, but its girth is not so great, seldom being more than twenty feet. Its dark wood is harder and finer grained than that produced by the Wych Elms. Its favour as a hedgerow tree is probably due to the fact that it gives shade which is not obnoxious to the growth of grass.

All three are subject to a great amount of variation, and in nurserymen's catalogues these forms have appropriate names, but they are not regarded as of sufficient permanence to merit scientific distinction. In point of age—Elms are known to exceed five hundred years.

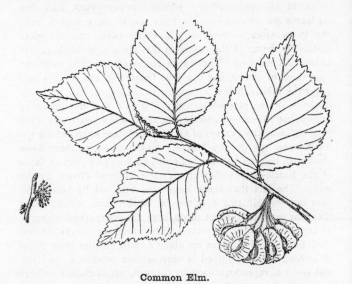

Common Elm.

Among the insects that feed upon the Elm's foliage, the most noteworthy is the caterpillar of the fine Large Tortoise-shell Butterfly (*Vanessa polychloros*). I have already mentioned the relationship subsisting between Elms and Nettles, and it is a point worth noting that nearly all our native species of *Vanessa* feed in the larval state upon the leaves of the Nettle. In London parks and squares the Elms are much infested

Pl. 38.

Common Elm—winter.

Pl. 39.

F 45.

Ash—summer.

by the caterpillars of the Vapourer-moth, whose wingless females may be seen like short-legged spiders on the bark, whilst the male flutters in an apparently aimless way on wings of rich brown with central white spots.

In October the leaves, which have for some time assumed a very dull dark-green tint, suddenly turn to orange, then fade to pale yellow, and fall in showers.

The name Elm was derived from the Latin *Ulmus*, and appears to indicate an instrument of punishment—probably from its rods having been used to belabour slaves. Prior remarks that the word is "nearly identical in all the Germanic and Scandinavian dialects, but does not find its root in any of them. It plays through all the vowels . . . but stands isolated as a foreign word which they have adopted." This "playing through the vowels" may be thus illustrated —Alm, Ælm, and Elm (Anglo-Saxon and English); Ilme, Olm, and Ulme, in various German dialects.

The Ash (*Fraxinus excelsior*).

So commanding, yet at the same time so light and graceful, does a well-grown Ash appear, that Gilpin called it the "Venus of the Woods." This may appear to some to be rather too close an approach to the "Lady of the Woods" (Birch), but in our opinion it well expresses the characteristics of the two. They are both exceedingly graceful, but the beauty of the Birch is that of the nymph, whilst that of the Ash is the combined grace and strength of the goddess. I have said "a well-grown" Ash, a phrase by which the timberman would understand a tree that had been hemmed in so closely by other trees that it has had no chance of developing as a tree, but only as a straight stout stick of wood, from eighty to one hundred feet long. *My* well-grown Ash is in a meadow, where both soil and atmosphere are moist and cool; where it has had elbow-room to reach its long graceful arms upwards and outwards, and to cover them with the plumy circlets of long leaves. It is there, or on the outskirts of the wood, or

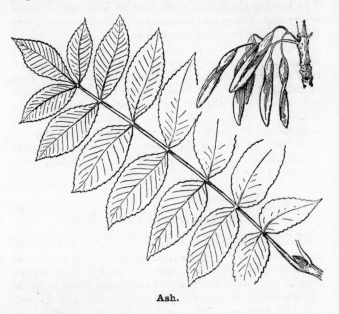

Ash.

in the hedgerow, that the Ash is able to do credit to Gilpin's name for it.

Before the reign of iron and steel was quite so universal, Ash timber was in demand for many uses where the metals have now supplanted it. It was then far more widely grown as a hedgerow tree than is now the case. Selby laments the neglect of this former custom, which kept up a supply of

Pl. 40.

Flowers of Ash,

Pl. 41.

G 47.

Bole of Ash.

tough and elastic timber, useful in all agricultural operations, and added much to the beauty of the country. No doubt the noxious drip and shade of the Ash have had much to do with this abandonment of it, for few things can live beneath it—a condition helped by its numerous fibrous roots, which quickly exhaust and drain the soil, and so starve out other plants. Although it thus drains the surface soil, it is not dependent upon these upper layers for food, for its much-branched roots extend very deeply in the porous soils it prefers.

It must not be supposed from the foregoing remarks that the Ash is confined to the lowlands. In Yorkshire it is found growing at an elevation of 1350 feet; in Mid-Germany it grows as far up as 3500 feet, and in the Alpine districts 500 feet higher still. It has a preference for the northern and eastern sides of hills, where the atmosphere is moist and cool, and the soil deep and porous, for it loves free and not stagnant moisture for its roots.

The bark of both trunk and branches is pale grey, and some look to this as the origin of the tree's English name. On examining the leafless branches in early spring, two things strike the observer—the blackness of the big opposite leaf-buds, and the stoutness of the twigs. This latter fact is due to the great size of the leaves they have to support, which implies a considerable strain in wind or rain. What are generally regarded as the leaves of the Ash are only leaflets, though they are equal in size to the leaves of most of our trees. The largest of the leaflets are about three inches in length, and there are from four to seven—mostly six—pairs, and an odd terminal one, to each leaf. They are lance-shaped, with toothed edges. The leaves are late in appearing, but, like Charles Lamb and his office-hours, they make up for it by an early departure.

The flowers of the Ash are very poor affairs, for they have

G

neither calyx nor corolla, though their association in large clusters makes them fairly conspicuous as they droop from the sides of the branches in April or May. Stamens and pistils are borne by the same or separate flowers, and both kinds or one only may be found on the same tree. The pistil is a greenish yellow pear-shaped body, and the stamens are very dark purple. The flowers are succeeded by bunches of "keys"—each one, when ripe, a narrow-oblong scale, with a notch at one end and a seed lying within at the other. The correct name for these is samaras. In looking at a bunch of these "keys"—they are something like the keys to the primitive locks of the ancients—one is struck by the fact that they all have a little twist in the wing or sail, which causes the "key" to spin steadily on the wind and reach the earth seed-end first. They are, therefore, sometimes known as "spinners." These are ripe in October; but though the trees produce seed nearly every year after the fortieth, one may chance to look at a dozen Ashes before he comes upon one that bears a seed. The reason for this lies in the fact that some trees have no female blossoms. The seeds do not germinate until the second spring after they are sown.

Much of the Ash-wood in use for carriage-poles, oars, axe and hammer shafts, and similar purposes where only small diameters are needed, are obtained from Ash-coppice, which rapidly produces well-developed poles. So strong and elastic is the Ash timber when taken from young trees, that it is claimed it will bear a greater strain than any other European timber of equal thickness. The Ash is not one of the long-lived trees, its natural span being about two hundred years, but its wood is regarded as best between the ages of thirty and sixty years.

Cattle and horses are fond of Ash leaves, which were formerly much used for fodder, and still are in some districts; but it is said that to indulge cows in this food is fatal to

Pl. 42

Ash—winter.

Pl. 43.

Field Maple.

the production of good butter from their milk. In some country places there is still extant a "Shrew-Ash"—a tree into which a hole has been bored sufficiently large to admit a living shrew-mouse, which has then been plugged in, to die of suffocation. A touch of a leaf from this tree was reputed to cure cramp, but especially that form of it supposed to be caused by a shrew passing over man or beast. Then there was the Ash whose bole had been cleft that it might be a "sovran" remedy for infantile hernia. It is difficult to account for the origin of these ideas, but they are deep-rooted and die hard. John Evelyn remarks of this latter super-stition: "I have heard it affirmed, with great confidence and upon experience, that the rupture, to which many children are obnoxious, is healed by passing the infant through a wide cleft in the bole or stem of a growing Ash-tree; it is then carried a second time round the Ash, and caused to repass the same aperture as before. The rupture of the child being bound up, it is supposed to heal as the cleft of the tree closes and coalesces."

The origin of the name Ash is uncertain, though many fanciful suggestions have been made in explanation of its meaning. Its Anglo-Saxon form was *æsc*, a word used by the same people for spear, but that was because their spear-shafts were made of Ash-wood.

The Maple (*Acer campestre*).

There are a number of Maples in cultivation, but only three of them are commonly met with in the open, and of these one alone is a native. This is the Small-leaved, Common, or Field Maple (*Acer campestre*), a small tree that attains a height of twenty to forty feet in the tall hedgerow or in the wood, but is most familiar as a mere bush or as a con-stituent of the low field-hedge. The bole of a large tree may be two feet thick, though it has no importance as timber, yet the turner, the cabinet-maker, and the artist in fancy pipes and snuff-boxes, are glad to make use of its fine-grained, pale-brown wood. This is often beautifully veined, especially the wood from the roots, and as it will take a high polish

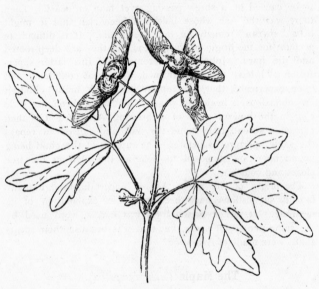

Field Maple.

which brings out these markings plainly, it is a very desirable wood for such purposes. The pale brown bark gives little clue to the character of the wood it covers, for in young trees it is rough and deeply fissured, though with age it becomes smooth.

Pl. 44.

Fruits of **Sycamore**.

Pl. 45.

Sycamore—summer.

The leaves vary greatly in size, those growing on a tree being much larger than those produced by a bush. They range from two to four inches in diameter, and are always in pairs—springing from the sides of the branch exactly opposite to each other. The general form of the leaf is kidney-shaped, but it is cut up into five lobes, which are more or less toothed. They are downy when young, of a deep green colour, but too frequently this is disguised by a thick layer of road-dust. In October they turn to a rich yellow, and the Maple is then prominent even in a distant view, for the bright colour of the foliage makes the tree stand out prominently, in strong contrast with the still deep green of the Oaks or Firs beyond.

The Maples are among the trees that have complete flowers, although in this case they happen to be greenish yellow. They are about a quarter of an inch across, have narrow sepals and narrower petals, eight stamens, and a two-lobed flattened ovary, that develops into the pair of broad-winged "keys," or samaras. These are individually much like those of the Ash, but unsymmetrical and curved, half an inch long, with their bases joined together. Sometimes in late summer these "keys" take on a colouring of deep crimson, previous to turning brown as they ripen. As a rule the contained seeds take eighteen months to germinate, though a few may start growth the first spring.

The Common Maple is thought to be indigenous only from the county of Durham to the southern coast, and in Ireland. In Scotland it is only an introduced plant that has become naturalized.

The Great Maple, Sycamore, or False Plane (*Acer pseudo-platanus*) is not a native tree, but it appears to have been introduced from the Continent as far back as the fifteenth century, so that it has had time during the intervening centuries to get well established among us, and by means of its winged seeds to distribute itself to remote corners of our islands. It appears to be fond of exposed situations, growing to a large size even near the sea, where the salt-laden gales destroy all other deciduous trees. Recently in Ireland we ascended a hill where the planting of pines and other trees had resulted

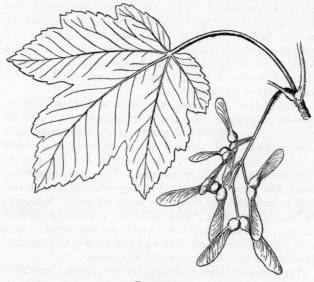

Sycamore.

in comparative failure, and found that the wind-borne seeds of the Sycamore had produced a large number of young trees, which will probably serve later as nurses for more desirable timber-producers. The close-grained, firm wood, which can be worked with ease, is not highly esteemed.

Its name of False Plane is due to the Scots calling it the

Leaf-buds of Sycamore.

Pl. 46.

Pl. 47.

Bole of Sycamore.

Plane, misled of old by the similarity of the leaves, and the fact that patches of the fine ash-grey bark flake off, as in the true Plane, showing other tints. It grows to a height of sixty or even eighty feet so quickly that it is full-grown when only fifty or sixty years old, though it is supposed to live from a hundred and fifty to two hundred and fifty years. Like that of the Common Maple, the wood of the Sycamore is firm and fine-grained, which does credit to the efforts of the French-polisher. The leaves are more heart-shaped, but cut into five lobes, whose edges are unequally toothed ; they are six or eight inches across. The flowers are similar to those of the Common Maple, but larger, and in a long hanging raceme, which has a rather fine appearance. The samaras are scimitar-shaped and red-brown, about an inch and a half long. These are produced freely after the tree is about twenty years old. Like many other Maples, the Sycamore has sap which contains much sugar. Some of this appears also to exude through the leaves, for they are often found to be quite sticky to the touch. The black patches so frequent on Sycamore leaves are the work of a small fungus— *Rhytisma acerinum.*

The Norway Maple (*Acer platanoides*) is a tree of much more recent (1683) introduction from the Continent. Its height is from thirty to sixty feet, and its early growth is very rapid. The leaves are even larger than those of Sycamore, of similar shape, but the lobes are only slightly toothed. The clusters of bright yellow flowers are almost erect ; the tree does not produce seed until it is between forty and fifty years old.

The Maple was the Mapel-treow or Mapulder of the Anglo-Saxons ; it was originally the Celtic *mapwl,* and the name indicated those knotty excrescences on the trunk from which the cabinet-maker got the mottled wood that was so highly prized in early times for the making of bowls and table-tops, for which fabulous prices have been paid.

The Poplars (*Populus*).

Almost everybody who has an elementary acquaintance with trees knows a Poplar at sight, the foliage being so very distinct from that of other trees. But the distinctions between the several species are not so immediately obvious. Five kinds of Poplar are commonly grown in this country, of which only two are regarded as distinct indigenous species. These are the White Poplar (*Populus alba*), and the Aspen (*P. tremula*). A third indigenous form, the Grey Poplar (*P. canescens*), is thought to be either a sub-species of *P. alba*, or a hybrid between that species and *P. tremula*. Then of common introduced species we have the Black Poplar (*Populus nigra*), and the Lombardy Poplar (*P. italica*).

The Poplars (*Populus*) and the Willows (*Salix*) together constitute the Natural Order *Salicaceæ*. The two genera agree broadly in the construction and arrangement of their flowers in catkins, but whereas the Poplars have broad leaves and drooping catkins, the Willows, with few exceptions, have long slender leaves and erect catkins. The sexes are not only in distinct flowers, but on separate trees—what botanists describe by the term *diœcious*. The males appear to be far more numerous than the females. In the popular sense there are no flowers, for there are neither sepals nor petals, each set of sexual organs being protected merely by a scale. The catkins containing these flowers usually appear before the leaves. As there is nothing to attract insects to the work, the trees have to rely upon the wind for conveying the pollen to the female trees. The first three species described below have from four to twelve stamens; *P. nigra* and *P. italica* have from twelve to twenty stamens. The Poplars share the love of the Willows for moist places. They are found more frequently in gardens and hedgerows than in woods. Their

Pl. 48.

Sycamore—winter.

Pl. 49. *H* 55.

White Poplar, with Catkins—spring.

growth is rapid, and their timber, consequently, is of little value, though its softness and lightness render it suitable for making boxes, and its whiteness and non-liability to splinter fit it for use as flooring. An additional point in favour of White Poplar for the latter purpose is its unreadiness to burn.

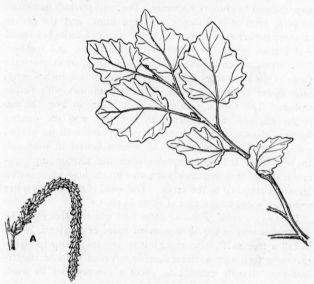

White Poplar, or Abele.

A, female catkin.

The White Poplar, or Abele (*Populus alba*), grows into a large tree, something between sixty and a hundred feet high, covered with smooth grey bark. Its branches spread horizontally, and its broad heart-shaped leaves, which vary from an inch to three inches long, are hung on long slender foot-stalks.

H

In most trees the leaf-stalks are flattened from above, but in the case of the Poplars they are flattened from the sides, so that when moved by the wind they flutter laterally. These leaves have a waved margin, a smooth upper surface, and are snowy white and cottony beneath. The leaf-buds are also invested by cottony filaments. The roots produce numerous suckers, even at a distance from the trunk, and the leaves on these sucker-shoots are very large—two to four inches broad —of a more triangular shape, the outline lobed and toothed. The catkins, which appear in March and April, are cylindrical ; those of the male trees may be as much as four inches long, each flower containing from six to ten stamens with purple anthers. The female catkins are not nearly so long, the two yellow stigmas are slender with slit tips, and the ovaries develop into slender egg-shaped capsules, each with its fringed scale. This species is said not to produce flowers in Scotland. In July, when the seed capsules open, the surrounding vegetation and ground are thickly strewn with the long white cotton filaments attached to the seeds. The wood of this tree is softer and more spongy than that of other Poplars.

The Grey Poplar (*Populus canescens*), which is thought to be indigenous only in the south-eastern parts of England, is not so tall a tree as *P. alba*, though it sometimes attains to eighty or ninety feet, with a circumference between ten and twenty-four feet. Its life extends to about a century, but its wood —which does not split when nails are driven through thin boards of it—is considered best between fifty and sixty years of age. The leaves on the branches are shaped like those of *P. alba*, but their under sides are either coated with grey down or are quite smooth ; those of the suckers have their margins cut into angles and teeth. The female flowers mostly have four wedge-shaped purple stigmas (sometimes two), which are cleft into four at their extremities.

The Aspen or Asp (*Populus tremula*) does not attain either

Pl. 50. *H* 56.

White Poplar—summer.

Pl. 51.

Bole of White Poplar.

to so large a size or so moderate an age as the Abele. Its
height, when full grown, is from forty to eighty feet, and after
fifty or sixty years its heart-wood begins to decay, and its
destruction is then hastened by the attacks of such internal-
feeding insects as the caterpillars of the Goat-moth and the

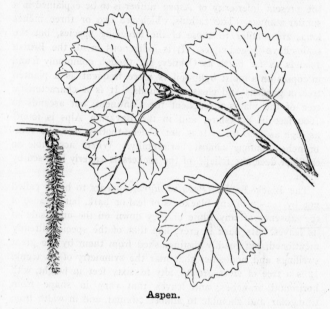

Aspen.

Wood Leopard-moth. The leaves on the branches are broadly
egg-shaped, approaching to round, the waved margin cut
into teeth with turned-in points. In one form (var. *villosa*)
the leaves are covered beneath with silky or cottony hairs ;
in the other form (var. *glabra*) they are almost smooth.
The leaves on the suckers are heart-shaped, without teeth.

The leaf-stalks of the Aspen are longer than those of its congeners, so that they are constantly on the flutter—a circumstance that has led to an explanatory legend, to the effect that the cross of Calvary was made of Aspen-wood, and that the tree shivers perpetually in remembrance. Possibly the present inferiority of Aspen timber is to be explained in a similar manner. The catkins, which are two or three inches long, are similar to those of the foregoing species, but the scales have jagged edges. It is indigenous in all the British Islands as far north as Orkney, but, though commonly found in copses on a moist light soil, is more frequent as a planted tree in gardens and pleasure grounds. It is a characteristic tree of the plains throughout the Continent, but ascends to 1600 feet in Yorkshire, and in the Bavarian Alps is found as high as 4400 feet. It is not a deep-rooting tree, the root-branches running almost horizontally. Where accessible to cattle or deer, the foliage of the suckers is eagerly browsed by them.

The Black Poplar (*Populus nigra*) appears to be so called not by reason of any blackness of leaf or bark, but because of the absence of any white or grey down on the underside of its leaves. Its bark is grey, like that of the species already mentioned, but readily distinguished from them by the great swellings and nodosities that mar the symmetry of its trunk. It is a tree of erect growth, fifty to sixty feet in height, with horizontal branches, and leaves that vary in shape from triangular and rhombic to almost circular, and in width from an inch to four inches. They have rounded teeth on the margins, which are at first also fringed, and in their young state the underside is silky. The flowers in the catkins of this and the next species are not so densely packed. Those of the male are two or three inches in length, and dark red in colour; their abundance before the tree has put out its leaves makes the male tree a conspicuous object. The female catkins

Pl. 52.

H 58.

Catkins of Aspen.

Pl. 53.

Black Poplar—summer.

Pl. 54.

Bole of Black Poplar

Pl. 55.

Black Poplar—winter.

are shorter and do not droop. When the roundish capsules
burst in May or June to distribute their seeds, the white cotton
with which the latter are invested gives prominence to the
female tree. The wood is chiefly used by the turner ; in
Holland, where it is extensively cultivated, it provides the
material for sabots. The Black Poplar is not regarded gene-

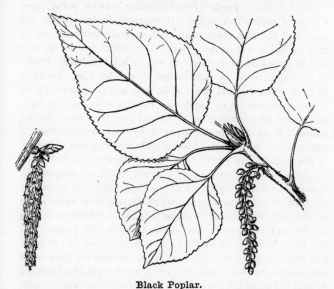

Black Poplar.

rally by botanists as a native of this country, but Prof. A.
Henry thinks it is really indigenous in the eastern counties
and in Wales, where it is found springing up on river banks
and in other moist situations. Some botanists regard it as
only a variety of the Lombardy Poplar, but apart from the
very different habit of the tree—not by itself sufficient grounds

for separation—there is the more important fact that the
Black Poplar rarely produces suckers from its roots, whilst
the Lombardy Poplar does so constantly. However, this is
a point we can leave for the botanists to discuss; for the
purposes of this book the two trees are sufficiently distinct
to be treated separately.

The Lombardy Poplar (*Populus italica*) was for many years
a tree of mysterious origin. It appeared in Italy about the
middle of the 18th century, and a botanical legend sprang up
that its home was in Asia, and that it ought not to be connected by name with Italy. It was called Lombardy Poplar
in consequence of its introduction thence by Lord Rochford
in 1758. The original was a male tree, and as practically all
of the vast number of Lombardy Poplars now existing have
descended from cuttings or suckers of that tree, they also are
males. It is now regarded as a hybrid resulting from a
natural cross between the Black Poplar and *Populus deltoidea*.
A few females are known to exist, and these are probably the
offspring of a later crossing. Its glossy leaves are shaped like
those of the Black Poplar, but its branches, instead of spreading,
all grow straight upwards, so that the fastigiate or spire shape
of the tree is produced—a shape only found otherwise among
coniferous trees, particularly in the Cypress, the Juniper and
the Irish Yew. It is its form, great height (100 to 150 feet),
and rapidity of growth that have led to its wide use here as an
ornamental tree—in many cases as a mere vegetable hoarding
to shut out some offensive view. Its growth is extremely rapid,
especially during its first score of years, when it will attain a
height of sixty feet or more, provided it be grown in good,
moist (but not marshy) soil. Its wood is, of course, of little
value, and is chiefly used for making boxes and packing-cases,
where its lightness, combined with toughness and cheapness,
is an advantage. The bark is rough and deeply furrowed,
unlike the other species; the furrows are spiral. Like the

Pl. 56.

Lombardy Poplar—summer.

Pl. 57.   *H* 61.

Bole of Lombardy Poplar.

Black Poplar, it has smooth shoots, and the unopened buds are sticky.

The Black Italian Poplar (*Populus deltoidea*) is another mis-named tree, for it is a native of North America, though introduced to England from the Continent in 1772 by Dr. John Hope. It has the distinction of being considered the most rapid-growing even of the Poplars. Loudon gives its rate of growth in the neighbourhood of London as between thirty and forty feet in seven years! Even in Scotland (where it has been largely planted as a substitute for Larch, since the partial failure of that tree) it attains a height of 120 feet in sixty years, when planted along the river banks. It is considered to be one of the parents of the Lombardy Poplar, from which the latter gets its erect habit.

The Tacamahac or Balsam Poplar (*Populus balsamifera*) is another importation from North America, introduced in 1692. In its native country it grows to a height of eighty feet, but here forty or fifty feet is more usual. Its leaves are of more slender form than those of the other Poplars, egg-shaped, with a near approach to being lance-shaped. Their edges are toothed, their upper surface dark green and smooth, the underside whitish with cotton. The distinctive character of the tree is the fragrance of its foliage, which scents the air on moist evenings, and makes the Tacamahac a desirable tree to plant near the water, where alone it attains any moderate size.

The Willows (*Salix*).

There is not in the whole of the British flora another genus of plants that presents such difficulties of identification as the genus *Salix*. Even so hardened a botanist as Sir J. D. Hooker, in reviewing the tangle of species, varieties (natural and cultivated), and hybrids, is so far stirred from his ordinary composure that he stigmatizes it as a "troublesome genus." When Sir Joseph chose that mild adjective he was at Kew surrounded by the national herbaria and with nicely labelled living plants at hand

for comparison. What, then, can the rambling nature-lover hope
to do with the Willows he comes across one at a time, without
much chance of comparing? He must be content to follow the
" lumpers," who group a number of these uncertain forms under
the name of a species to which they have evident relationship.
When he has mastered the distinctions between these aggregate
species, it will be early enough to attempt the segregation of the
forms and varieties under each.

In their natural condition Willows are graceful and picturesque,
but a large number of the examples met with in our rambles
have been so altered for commercial reasons as to be more
grotesque than beautiful. It is not the timber-man who is
responsible this time, for a pollard Willow, though it produces a
shock-head of long slender shoots, suitable for basket-rods, lets
in moisture at the top of the bole, and the wood is more or less
decayed and worthless. Only four of our native Willows can be
regarded as timber trees. These are the White Willow, the
Crack Willow, the Bedford Willow, and the Sallow. Like the
Poplars, their growth is very rapid, and their wood is consequently light, but it has the advantage of Poplar-wood in being
tougher, and therefore serving for purposes where Poplar is of no
value. In the present day the growers of straight-boled Willows
find their best market among the makers of cricket-bats. A good
deal of it is also cut into thin strips for plaiting into chip-hats
and hand-baskets. The Osier is grown in extensive riverside
beds for the production of long pliant shoots for the basket-
weavers; though many of the so-called Osier-rods are really
stool-shoots from Willows that have been pollarded, or whose
leading shoot has never been allowed to grow. On those parts
of our coast where the crab and lobster fishery is pursued, a
regular supply of such shoots for weaving into " pots " and
" hullies " is a necessity, and a " withy bed " will usually be found
on some valley stream near, or on a damp terrace halfway up
the cliffs.

Pl 58.

Lombardy Poplar—winter.

Pl. 59.

Crack Willow—summer.

Pl. 60.

Bole of Crack Willow.

Pl. 61.

Crack Willow—winter.

The bark of the tree Willows has long been known to be rich in an alkaloid called *salicine,* which has tonic and astringent properties, and has often been used instead of *quinine,* though it is not nearly so powerful as the Peruvian drug. The bark is also used for tanning.

The association of the Willow with sadness is very old, but there does not appear to be any satisfactory reason for it—certainly to contemplate a naturally-grown Willow that grows on the edge of a limpid stream, in which its graceful shoots and slender leaves are reflected, does not suggest sad thoughts to the average healthy mind. The association is chiefly with maidens forsaken by their false lovers, as indicated by Shakespeare when he makes Desdemona say—

> " My mother had a maid called Barbara :
> She was in love ; and he she loved proved mad,
> And did forsake her ; she had a song of ' Willow ' ;
> An old thing 'twas, but it expressed her fortune,
> And she died singing it."

The Crack Willow or Withy (*Salix fragilis*) is one of the two most considerable of our tree Willows. In good soil it will in twenty years attain nearly its full height, which is eighty or ninety feet. Its bole sometimes has a girth of twenty feet. Its smooth, polished shoots afford the best ready means of distinguishing it, for instead of their base pointing to the centre of the trunk as in other trees, they grow obliquely, so that the shoots frequently cross each other. They are both tough and pliant, but if struck at the base they readily break off. This character explains the names Crack Willow and *fragilis*. The leaves are lance-shaped, three to six inches long, smooth, with glandular teeth, pale or glaucous on the underside, and with half-heart-shaped stipules, which, however, are soon cast off. As we have already indicated under the head of Poplars, the male and female catkins of the Willows are borne by different trees. In the case of the Crack Willow, the male catkins are an inch or two long, proportionately stout, each

I

flower bearing two stamens (occasionally three, four, or five). The female catkin is more slender, the flowers each containing a smooth ovary, ending in a short style that divides into two curved stigmas. The catkins appear in April or May. Although, like most of the Willows, this species is fond of cold, wet soil in low

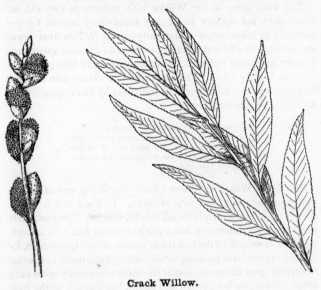

Crack Willow.

situations, it is not restricted to the plains. In Northumberland it is found at 1300 feet above the sea. Its northward range extends as far as Ross-shire, but it is a doubtful native in both Scotland and Ireland.

The Bedford Willow (*S. viridis*) is believed to be a hybrid between *S. fragilis* and *S. alba*. It grows to a height of fifty feet, with a girth of twelve feet. The leaves are more slender

Pl. 62.

White Willow—summer.

Pl. 63.

Flowers of White Willow.

than those of *S. fragilis*, taper to a point at each end, and are very smooth on both sides. It occurs in swampy woods.

The White Willow (*Salix alba*) is so called from the appearance of the leaves as the light is reflected from their silky surfaces, which are alike above and below. It is a tree from sixty to

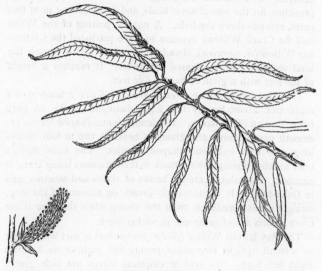

White Willow.

eighty feet high, with a girth of twenty feet, covered with thick and deeply fissured bark. The leaves are from two to four inches long, of a narrow elliptical shape. In the typical form the twigs are olive-coloured, but in the variety *vitellina* (known as the Golden Willow) these are yellow or reddish. In the hybrid *cœrulea* the old leaves become quite smooth above, but retain the glaucous appearance of the underside. The White Willow is found as far north as Sutherlandshire, but although it is believed to be an indigenous species, most of the modern specimens appear to have been planted. It affords good timber, and the bark is almost equal to that of Oak for tanning. A great number of the old Willows met with in our rambles are partially decayed, a condition frequently the result of lopping large branches, for the wound never heals, and decay setting in at that point, extends down the bole. A natural pairing of the White and the Crack Willows appears to have produced the Cricket-bat Willow (*S. cœrulea*), already referred to, which is now the kind most frequently planted for timber. It reaches a height of 100 feet with a girth of four or five feet.

The Almond-leaved or French Willow (*Salix triandra*) is a small tree about twenty feet high, distinguished by its bark being thrown off in flakes. Its slender lance-shaped leaves are smooth green above and glaucous beneath, two to four inches long, and with half-heart-shaped stipules. The male flowers offer another distinguishing mark in their stamens being three in number. Its habitats are the banks of rivers and streams, and in Osier-beds. It is extensively grown on account of the long, straight shoots produced from the stump when the tree is cut down, which are of great use in wicker-work.

The Bay-leaved Willow (*Salix pentandra*) is met with either as a small upright tree about twenty feet high, or as a shrub eight feet high. Its oval or elliptical leaves are rich green, smooth and sticky on the upper surface, and give out a pleasant fragrance like those of the Bay-tree ; they vary from an inch to four inches long, and they may or may not bear stipules, but if these are present they will be egg-shaped or oblong. The stamens are normally five in each flower, but they vary up to twelve. This is reputed to be of all our Willows the latest to flower. A line drawn through York, Worcester, and North Wales will give roughly its southward range as a native species. South of that line it has been planted ; north of it to the Scottish

Pl. 64

Bole of White Willow.

White Willow—winter

Pl. 65.

Pl. 66.

Almond-leaved Willow—summer.

Pl. 67.

Almond-leaved Willow—winter.

border it is a native. It has been found growing at a height of 1300 feet in Northumberland.

The Sallow (*Salix caprea*) is the only other species that can properly be considered as a tree, as it attains to a height of thirty feet, though fifteen to twenty feet is a more common

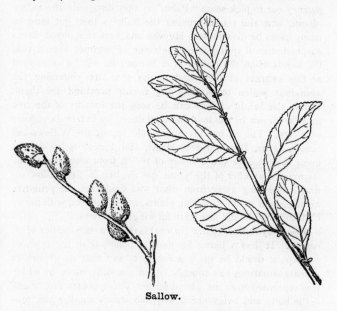

Sallow.

measurement. Its usually egg-shaped leaves vary from almost round to elliptical or lance-shaped, and from two to four inches in length. In the typical form, which occurs chiefly in woods, dry pastures, and hedgerows, they are broad, smooth, and dull-green above, covered with soft white down beneath ; the stipules half-kidney-shaped. This is the earliest of all our

Willows to flower, and the gold (male) and silver (female) catkins are put out before the leaves. In the country, within a few miles of the larger cities, this can hardly be a desirable species to plant, for on the Sunday before Easter thousands who at no other period exhibit any strong religious tendency journey out to pick some " Palm," as they designate the Sallow bloom, and the rough pruning the Sallows then get must in many cases be disastrous. He who imagines that insect life is suspended until spring is on the verge of summer should visit the woods when the Sallow is in bloom ; he will be astonished at the swarms of bees and moths that are collecting the abundant pollen or sipping the nectar provided for them. Before the bright catkins can be seen the locality of the tree may be known by the loud hum produced by hundreds of pairs of wings. The all but invariable rule among the Willows—as among Oaks, Beech, Birch, Hazel, and Pines—is to depend upon the wind for the transfer of pollen from one tree to the stigmas of another of the same species, but in the Sallow we find a breaking away from what was doubtless the primitive arrangement in all flowering plants, by the bribing with honey of more reliable and less wasteful winged carriers.

The Gray Sallow (*Salix cinerea*) is really a sub-species of *S. caprea*. It has a liking for moister places than the type, or perhaps it would be more accurate to say that its growth in moister situations has brought about the differences by which it is separated from the parent form. These points are, briefly —the buds and twigs are downy, the leaves smaller and proportionately narrower, the upper surface downy, grey-green beneath ; the anthers of the male pale yellow, the capsule of the female smaller.

The Eared Sallow (*S. aurita*) is probably also only another form of *S. caprea*, distinguished by its small, bushlike proportions (two to four feet high), long branches and red twigs ; its small wrinkled leaves, which are usually less that two inches

Pl. 68.

Bay-leaved Willow—summer.

Pl. 69.   *I* 69.

Bay-leaved Willow—winter.

long, are of an almost oblong shape, downy beneath, and with large ear-shaped stipules. Its likeness is much closer to *S. cinerea* than to the type ; it is fond of damp copses and moist places on heaths, where it may be found at considerable elevations. In the Highlands it ascends to 2000 feet.

There are Willows of dwarf habit, some with long straggling branches and more or less prostrate stems, that grow upon heaths. Each has a name under which it has at some time or other been ranked as a distinct species, just as the forms of Bramble and Rose have been. The differences between them are minute, and of little interest save to the advanced scientific botanist, who with his dried specimens spread before him often detects subtle distinctions not apparent to the out-door student of the living plant. For the purposes of those for whom this volume is intended they may be regarded as one.

Dwarf Silky Willow (*Salix repens*). It is a low bush from six to twelve inches high, the stem lying along the ground. Some of the branches straggle in the same fashion, but those which bear the flowers are more or less erect. The leaf-buds and the young leaves are silky, a condition that usually endures on the lower surface, and in some forms on the upper also. They are broadly or narrowly lance-shaped, varying in the different forms alluded to above ; in size they range from a half to one and a half inches in length, and may have lance-shaped stipules, or none at all. The scales of the catkins are yellowish-green or purple, with dark tips. After they have shed their pollen the anthers turn black. One form or other of this species will be found in all parts of the British Islands where there are heaths or commons ; in the Highlands it occurs as high as 2500 feet.

Another group of small Willows that form bushes (rarely a small tree) have been united under two species—the Dark-leaved Willow (*Salix nigricans*) and the Tea-leaved Willow

(*Salix phylicifolia*). None of them occur south of Yorkshire, and the chief distinction between the two species (?) consists in the leaves of *S. nigricans* turning black when being dried for the herbarium, whilst those of *S. phylicifolia* do not.

The Osier (*Salix viminalis*). Many of the foregoing Willows,

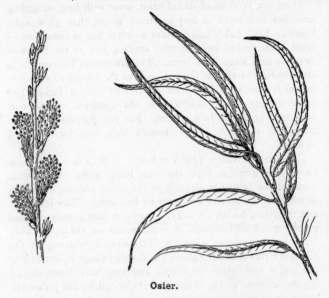

Osier.

when cut down low and induced to send out long, slender shoots, are known as Osiers, but only two species are botanically regarded as Osiers—this and the Purple Osier (*S. purpurea*). The present species may remain as a shrub or grow into a small tree, thirty feet high, with long, straight branches, which are silky when young, but afterwards become polished. The leaves vary in length from four to ten inches, and are slenderly lance-

Pl 70.

Bole of Bay-leaved Willow.

Pl. 71.

Purple Osier—summer.

shaped, tapering to a point in front, and narrowing into the
foot-stalk behind. They have waved margins without teeth,
and the upper surface netted with veins, the under surface
silvery and silky ; stipules narrow lance-shaped. The Osier
may be seen in Osier-beds and wet places generally throughout
the country as far north as Elgin and Argyll. There are
several varieties and hybrids.

The Purple Osier (*Salix purpurea*). In all the other
Willows mentioned the stamens, whatever their number, all
have the filaments distinct from each other. In this species
alone the filaments of the two stamens are more or less
united. The Purple Osier gets its name from the red or purple
bark which clothes the thin but tough twigs. It is a shrub,
and grows from five to ten feet high. The leaves, which are
rather thin in texture, are from three to six inches long, of slender-
lance-shape, with toothed edges, smooth and glaucous on both
sides, but especially beneath, somewhat hairy when young.
They are almost opposite on the twigs, and when dried for the
herbarium turn black. There are several varieties of this shrub,
which were formerly honoured with specific rank.

There remains a group of several small species of very local
occurrence, with which we can do little more here beyond
naming them.

The Woolly Willow (*Salix lanata*) is a small shrub, two or three
feet high, with twisted branches, woolly twigs, and hairy black
buds. The broad egg-shaped or oblong leathery leaves are also
woolly, and two or three inches long. There are half-heart-shaped
stipules at the base of the very short leaf-stalk. It is an Alpine
plant, and is found about the mountain rills of Perth, Forfar,
Inverness, and Sutherland at elevations between 2000 and 2500
feet. Conspicuous in spring for its rich golden catkins. Sadler's
Willow (*S. sadleri*), of which only two or three specimens have
been found (in Glen Callater, 2500 feet), is probably a form of
this species.

K

The Lapland Willow (*Salix lapponum*) is of a similar proportion to the last-named, sometimes erect, sometimes trailing. Its leaves are more elliptic in shape, covered above with silky hairs and below with cottony filaments. In *lanata* the raised veins form a network pattern; in *lapponum* they are straight. The stipules at the base of the long foot-stalk are small or altogether wanting. Like the preceding species, it is restricted to Scotch Alpine rocks, at elevations between 2000 and 2700 feet.

The Whortle-leaved Willow (*Salix myrsinites*) is a small, wiry, creeping, or half-erect shrub, six inches to a foot high, with toothed, dark glossy leaves, an inch or less in length, whose net-veining shows on both sides. It is restricted to the Alpine parts of mid-Scotland, from 1000 to 2700 feet.

The Small Tree-Willow (*Salix arbuscula*) is a small shrub, whose stem creeps along the ground and roots as it goes, sending up more or less erect branches a foot or two high. The downy twigs are first yellow, then reddish-brown. The small leaves vary from egg-shaped to lance-shaped, and are shining above and glaucous beneath; toothed. In the Highlands of Aberdeen, Argyll, Dumfries, Forfar, and Perth, between 1000 and 2400 feet.

The Least Willow (*Salix herbacea*) is not so restricted in its range, for it is found in all parts of the United Kingdom where there are heights sufficiently Alpine (2000 to 4300 feet) for its tastes. It is only an inch or two high, and has consequently the distinction of being the smallest British shrub. It is not so herbaceous as it seems, or as its name implies, for its shrubby stem and branches creep along underground, sending up only short, scantly leaved twigs. The curled, roundish leaves do not exceed half an inch in length; they are net-veined, toothed, and shining. The catkins appear after the leaves.

The Net-leaved Willow (*Salix reticulata*) is another of the Scotch Alpines. It is similar in habit to the last-named, but

Pl. 72.

Purple Osier—winter.

Pl. 73.

Yew.

larger, its buried branches sending up twigs a foot long. The roundish-oblong, leathery leaves are not toothed ; they are smooth above and glaucous beneath, strongly net-veined on either side. The purplish or yellow catkins do not develop till after the leaves. It is restricted to the mountains of Aberdeen, Forfar, Inverness, Perth, and Sutherland.

The Weeping Willow (*Salix babylonica*), so conspicuous an ornament of riverside lawns, is an introduced species, whose slender branches hang downwards. It has large, lance-shaped, finely toothed leaves, smooth above and glaucous beneath. Further description of so well-known a tree is unnecessary. It attains a height of forty to fifty feet. The name *babylonica* was bestowed in the belief that its headquarters were on the banks of the Euphrates. It is now known to be a native of Japan, and other parts of Asia.

The name Willow is the Anglo-Saxon *welig*, indicating pliancy, willingness.

Our Native Conifers.

The British flora is singularly poor in coniferous plants, the Scots Pine, the Yew, and the Juniper being our only native species, and even of these some authorities will have it that the Yew is not truly a Conifer at all; they place it in a separate order—*Taxaceæ*. For our present purpose, however, although the Yew does not produce cones, it will be convenient to keep it in its old position. The principal feature distinguishing all Conifers and their allies (*Gymnosperms*) from other flowering plants (*Angiosperms*) is briefly this : Angiosperms have their incipient seeds (*ovules*) enclosed in a carpel, through which a shoot from the pollen grain has to penetrate in order to reach and fertilize the ovule. In Gymnosperms the carpel takes the form of a leaf or bract, upon which the naked ovule lies open to actual

contact with the pollen grain. After fertilization the carpel en-
larges to protect the seed, and becomes fleshy or woody, in the
latter case a group of carpels forming the well-known cones of
Pine or Fir.

In some of the groups (as the Yew, for example) the male or
pollen-producing flowers are borne by a separate tree from that
which bears the female or cone-producing flowers. In the Pines
both sexes are found on the same tree ; but throughout the order
the pollen is carried by the wind. All the species are trees or
shrubs. They are among the most valuable of timber trees, and,
in addition, yield a number of useful substances, such as pitch,
tar, turpentine, etc. The leaves are always rigid, extremely
narrow, and long in proportion : usually of the form that botanists
term linear, with the two sides parallel. In the Yews these leaves
spread out in two rows from opposite sides of the twigs ; in the
Pines they are in clusters of two, three, or five, seeming to
be bound together at the base by a wisp of thin skin. The
number of leaves in each bundle is often a help in distinguishing
species.

The Yew (*Taxus baccata*) lacks the graceful proportions of
most of our trees, but it has for compensation a most obvious air
of strength and endurance. Who doubts, as he gazes at some
sombre Yew in the old churchyard, the story of the local
antiquarian, who tells him the tree has so stood for 2000 years. He
may, perhaps, mildly suggest that neither the church nor the
churchyard was in existence so far back, but even then the
antiquarian will probably have the last word by suggesting that
the grove of Yews of which this formed part was the church of
the past. Thousands see in cathedral aisles the reproduction in
stone of the pine-forest or the beech-wood. Standing before an
ancient Yew they may see whence came the idea for those
clustered columns. They actually exist in the bole of the Yew,
which presents the appearance not of a single trunk, but of
several trunks that have coalesced. This condition is due to the

Yew continually pushing out new shoots from the lower part of its bole, which take an upright direction, and coalesce with the old wood.

Although the Yew is a large tree, it is by no means a tall tree: the height of full-grown Yews in this country ranging between fifteen and fifty feet, though they are said to attain a greater length in India. The bole of the Yew is short but massive, covered with a thin red bark, that flakes off in patches much after the manner of Plane-bark. Large specimens have a girth of from twenty-five to fifty feet—or even more. Such a circumference represents the growth of many centuries, for the annual growth-rings are very thin. It is this very slow growth that produces the hard, compact, and elastic wood that was so highly esteemed in the days of the long-bow. Not only is the timber elastic and strong, but it is exceedingly durable, so that it is said, "A post of Yew will outlast a post of iron." Its branches start from the trunk at only a few feet from the ground, and, taking an almost horizontal direction, throw out a great number of leafy twigs, which provide a dense and extensive shade. These leaves are leathery in texture, curved somewhat after the manner of a reaping-hook, shiny and dark above, pale and unpolished below.

We have already mentioned that the Yew is a diœcious tree —that is, one whose male and female blossoms are borne on separate trees—but the statement requires qualification to this extent, that occasionally a tree will be found bearing a branch or branches whose flowers are of the sex opposite to those covering the greater part of the tree. The male catkin is almost round, a quarter of an inch across, and contains about half a dozen yellow anthers, the base surrounded by dry overlapping scales. They may be found during February and March, in profusion on the underside of the boughs. The female flower is much smaller, and consists of a fleshy disk with a few scales at its base, and on this stands a single seed-egg. After fertilization of the seed-egg the disk develops into a red wax-like cup around the enlarging seed with its olive-green coat. The flesh of the cup is full of sweet mucilage, which makes the fruit acceptable to children, but the flavour is rather too mawkish to suit older tastes. Yew-berries are not poisonous, as sometimes supposed; neither is the contained kernel, which has a pleasant nutty flavour. Much has

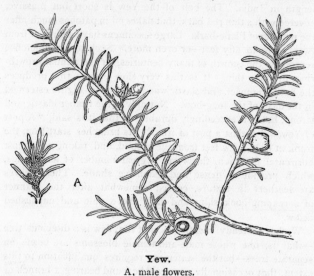

Yew.

A, male flowers.

been said and written as to the toxic property of Yew-leaves, and it appears that though cattle and goats may eat them, often with impunity, horses and human beings pay the penalty of death for such indulgence. That word toxic, by the way, owes its significance to the Yew. The tree was named *taxus* in Latin, from the Greek *toxon* (a bow), because of the ancient repute of its wood for making that instrument. The tree was held to be

Pl. 74.

Bole of Yew.

Pl. 75.

Juniper.

poisonous, and so its name in the form of *toxicum* came to designate all poisons.

There are some lines in *In Memoriam* which many readers of Tennyson have found as obscure as the shade of the Yew where they were conceived. The poet is addressing a venerable churchyard Yew in these words :—

> " Old warder of these buried bones,
> And answering now my random stroke
> With fruitful cloud and living smoke ;
> Dark Yew, that graspest at the stones
> And dippest towards the dreamless dead,
> To thee, too, comes the golden hour,
> When flower is feeling after flower."

To any readers who have found a difficulty in understanding these lines, we would say : visit the Yew groves in February or March, when the male branches are thickly covered with their yellow flowers, and strike a branch with your stick. In response to the "random stroke" the pollen will fly off in a "fruitful cloud" or "living smoke," some of it to be caught by the minute female blossoms. This is the Yew-tree's "golden hour, when flower is feeling after flower."

In the pre-gunpowder era, so important was it to have a sufficient supply of suitable wood for the making of the dreaded English long-bow, that the culture of the Yew was made the subject of a number of royal ordinances, which, of course, were allowed to drop out of observance when the bow was displaced by the firearm. And now when men plant Yews they are mostly the ornamental varieties, such as the Irish or Florence Court Yew, which originated as a wild sport on the mountains of Fermanagh about a hundred and fifty years ago. Evelyn, it is true, revived the interest in the Yew as an ornamental tree, and it is with regret we add that at his suggestion it was first put to the base use called topiary work, which had hitherto been restricted to Box and Juniper. Evelyn showed how much more closely and continuously the Yew could be clipped without affecting its vitality, and the fashion he thus set—and regarded as a "merit"—was very generally followed during the next century. Many of the atrocities of those days are still with us, but only as survivals ; and we can so often agree with Evelyn that we may forgive him for having led our ancestors astray in this matter. Evelyn was by no means blind to the good points of the tree in its natural condition, as witness this quotation, which is as true to-day as when it was written :—

"He that in winter should behold some of our highest hills in Surry clad with whole woods of these two last sorts of trees [Box and Yew], for divers miles in circuit (as in those delicious groves of them, belonging to the Honourable, my Noble Friend, the late Sir Adam Brown, of Bechworth Castle), from Box Hill, might, without the least violence to his imagination, easily fancy himself transported into some new or enchanted country ; for if in any spot in England,

'tis here
Eternal spring and summer all the year."

Along the chalk range of which the celebrated Box Hill forms part will be found many fine examples of the Yew, as at Cherkley Court, near Leatherhead, where there is an actual Yew forest. There was a monstrous Yew at Brabourne in Kent, in Evelyn's time, for he tells us he measured it, and found its girth to be only one inch short of fifty-nine feet. There are numerous giants of the species still living in quiet country churchyards, where they have probably served—as tradition states of those at Fountains Abbey—as a shelter for the builders of the ancient church during its erection. It is reputed to be the longest-lived of all trees, and it is to be hoped that no hindrance will be put in the way of these connections of the present with the far past living to their full natural limit, whatever it may be. It is naturally a tree of the uplands and lower hills, and shows a distinct preference for soils that contain plenty of lime.

Pl. 76.   Fruits of Yew.

Pl. 77.

Fruits of Juniper.

The Irish Yew (var. *fastigiata*), to which passing reference was made, differs from the type in having all its branches growing erectly, after the manner of a Lombardy Poplar, and in the leaves being scattered promiscuously over the branchlets instead of being in two regular rows. It attains a height of twenty to twenty-five feet.

The Juniper (*Juniperus communis*) is seldom more than a shrub a few feet in height, though it occasionally develops into a small tree from ten to twenty feet high, and with a girth of five feet. It has a fibrous red bark, which flakes off like that of the Yew. The leaves are shaped like a cobbler's awl, rigid, and end in sharp points. They have thickened margins, the concave upper sides are glaucous, and they are arranged round the branches in whorls of three. The male and female flowers are on separate trees. The male catkin may be known in May by its numerous anthers and pale yellow pollen. The female catkins will be found in the axils of the leaves, and resemble buds. The scales are fleshy, and after fertilization the upper ones slowly develop into the form of a berry, which has a few undeveloped scales at its base. They do not ripen until the following year, when they are blue-black, covered with a fine glaucous bloom. They have a pungent flavour, which is utilized in concocting gin, which indeed owes its name to this fact—the word being merely a contraction of *genévrier*, the French form of Juniper. The "berries" have long been known as a kidney stimulant—a fact which has been fully utilized as the justification of every gin-drinker. A beautiful little moth—*Hypsilophus marginellus*—may often be taken about the Juniper, upon which its caterpillar feeds.

To appreciate the variety of forms assumed by the Juniper according to the elevation at which it grows, it should be seen on slopes like those of the North Downs in Surrey—one portion of the range at Mickleham is named Juniper Hill. In the valleys it may be found as a small shapely tree, higher up the

L

slopes as a pyramidal shrub, and as we reach higher and more
exposed positions, the Juniper gradually dwindles to a low,
shapeless bush. This, however, must not be confounded with a
distinct variety to which the name *nana* has been applied; it

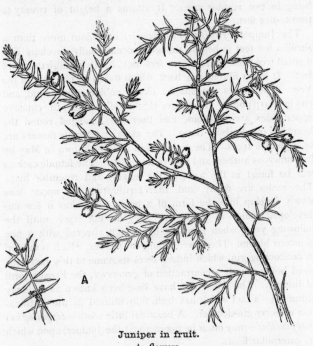

Juniper in fruit.
A, flowers.

differs from the type in having shorter and broader overlapping
leaves, with curved tips. Var. *nana* is confined to the mountains of the north of our islands, and ascends to 2700 feet, which
is 300 feet higher than is recorded of the type.

Pl. 78.

Scots Pine.

Pl. 79.

Bole of Scots Pine.

The Virginian Juniper (*Juniperus virginiana*), or "Red Cedar,"[1] as it is called on the American continent, is a much larger plant, which is frequently planted in our parks and gardens. It varies in habit, and may be low and spreading, bush-like, or tall and tapering, thirty to forty feet high. Its leaves are in threes, like those of our native species, but the three are united by their bases. It is with the red heart-wood of this tree that our "cedar" pencils are covered, large quantities of the timber of *J. virginiana*, and formerly of *J. bermudiana*, being imported for the purpose. The Virginian Juniper has been with us for many years. It is mentioned by Evelyn in his "Sylva" (1664), and is believed to have been introduced by him from North America.

The Scots Pine (*Pinus sylvestris*), commonly but incorrectly styled Scotch Fir, is the typical Pine-tree of Northern Europe, where (especially in Russia and Northern Germany) it constitutes huge forests. It is even said to cover far wider tracts of country than any other forest tree. Although there is evidence that in ancient days it was pretty widely distributed over Britain, to-day all those Pine-woods of Southern England are the results of planting, and it is only in a few places between Yorkshire and Sutherland, and in Ireland, that it can be regarded as truly wild and indigenous. Mr. John Nisbet points out that the term "pine-forest" is a bit of tautology, for the old German word *forst* was derived from *foraha*—now represented by *föhre*, a fire or pine—so that "pine-forest" is equivalent to "pine-pine." However, the etymologists will probably allow us to speak of Pine-woods, and we will try to remember that when we use the word forest it must always indicate an assemblage of Pine-trees.

In favourable soil, at a moderate elevation, the Scots Pine is a fine tree a hundred feet high, with a rough-barked trunk, whose girth is twelve feet. Under such conditions it develops a strong tap-root, which goes deep; but where the soil is shallow or otherwise unfavourable the tap-root is not developed. At great elevations the upward growth is checked early, and it becomes a mere evergreen bush. The branches are short and spreading, those on the lower portions of the trunk dying early, so that the tree soon gets that gaunt weather-beaten look that is so characteristic of it. Then, after the growth of the leading shoot has become feeble, the upper branches continue to lengthen, and so bring about that flat-topped condition. Its growth is rapid, and in twenty years it will attain a height of forty or fifty feet.

The leaves, which are in bundles of two, are from two to three inches long, very slender, grooved above and convex beneath. They remain on the tree for over two years, and in their first season are of a glaucous hue, but in the second year this changes to dark deep-green. Both male and female flowers are borne by the same tree. The male catkins are individually small ($\frac{1}{4}$ inch), but are combined in spikes ; this and the abundant pale yellow pollen makes them conspicuous. The female cones are somewhat egg-shaped, tapering to a point, which is often curved. They are usually in clusters of three, and grow to a length of two or three inches. The scales are comparatively few, and their ends are thickened into an irregular four-sided boss, at first ending in a little point. The seeds are winged, and contained beneath the scales. They take about eighteen months to ripen, when the scales separate in dry windy weather, and allow the breeze to pick out the seeds and send them flying through the air to a great distance. The pollen, too, it should be noted, is of a form specially fitted for aerial transport, each particle of pollen forming two connected spheres. It is quite a common experience in May to find little heaps of this pollen collected in hollows and at the margins of ponds in the neighbourhood of Pine-woods ; but, so difficult is it to get people to understand the common facts of nature, that it is generally regarded as evidence of a shower of brimstone having fallen. It is not only the ignorant rustic who falls into this error ; judging from letters sent to the press by country parsons, even the universities fail to prepare their alumni to deal with

such phenomena.   After the eruptions of La Soufriere, several
wrote to say that quantities of powdered sulphur from St.
Vincent had descended in their Surrey and Hampshire parishes !

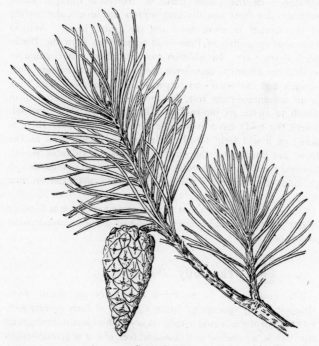

Scots Pine.

their notion being that the commercial " flowers of sulphur " are
the direct produce of volcanoes.

Although the wood produced by the Scots Pine in this country
is not considered of the highest quality, the species is certainly

of equal value as a timber-producer with any other tree. Owing to our mild winters and long periods of seasonal growth, the Pine-wood produced in Britain is coarse-grained and not very durable. In the colder parts of Northern Europe, where summers are short and the long winters are severe, the texture of the timber is more solid and the grain closer. And so enormous quantities of Pine-wood come to us from the Baltic ports every year. In addition to the timber, other valuable substances known to commerce are products of the Scots Pine —pitch and tar, resin and turpentine, for example. The Pine is an accommodating tree, for though it likes a deep soil in which to strike its tap-root, it will grow upon rocky ground, where the roots have to become horizontal and near the surface ; or it will form forests on poor sandy soils, even on the loose hot sands near the seashore. This is a valuable power, because the fall of its needles gradually forms a humus, and so provides food for other plants which could not exist on raw sand.

Other coniferous trees that have become more or less familiar in our plantations and parks will be found in the second division of this book.

The Holly (*Ilex aquifolium*).

The Holly must be regarded as one of our small trees, although many specimens attain a height of forty or fifty feet, with a girth of ten or twelve feet. It is well distributed throughout our islands, ascending to a thousand feet, and it is probable that no other tree is so well known, by its foliage at least, as the Holly, or Holm, to give it its ancient name. The word Holm was incorporated by some of our ancestors far back in the name Holmsdale, which still attaches to the stretch of country at the southern foot of the chalk hills in Surrey, and whose proud motto is, " Never wonne, ne never shall." At the western end

Male Flowers of Scots Pine.

Pl. 80.

Pl. 81.

Holly.

of the Holmsdale is Holmwood, and still a little further west
Holmbury. In these places the Holly still grows bravely, not
far from the old home of John Evelyn, who must be thought of
whenever we talk of Hollies, though the recollection has to do
with Sayes Court, his Thames-side house, where the barbarian

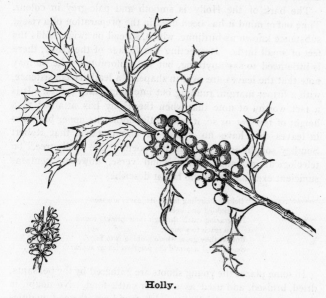

Holly.

Peter wrought such havoc with his cherished Holly-hedge. How
Evelyn must have lamented that outrage is indicated in this
extract from the "Sylva" :—

"Is there under heaven a more glorious and refreshing object
of the kind, than an impregnable hedge of about four hundred feet
in length, nine feet high, and five in diameter, which I can show
in my now ruined gardens at Say's Court (thanks to the Czar of

Moscovy) at any time of the year, glittering with its armed and varnished leaves? The taller standards at orderly distance, blushing with their natural coral. It mocks the rudest assaults of the weather, beasts, or hedge-breakers, *et illum nemo impunè lacessit.*"

The bark of the Holly is smooth and pale-grey in colour. Time out of mind it has been used in the preparation of a viscid substance known as birdlime, which, spread on twigs, holds the feet of small birds. Respecting the foliage of the Holly, there is little need to say anything, but for uniformity's sake we may note that the leaves are oval in shape, of a leathery consistence, with a firmer margin, running out into long sharp spines. It is a fact worthy of note that when the Holly has attained to a height of ten feet or so, it frequently clothes its upper branches in leaves that have no spines—a circumstance that Robert Southey sought to explain in his poem "The Holly-tree," on teleological grounds. His second verse, however, contains sufficient explanation of the fact it describes :—

> " Below, a circling fence, its leaves are seen
>   Wrinkled and keen ;
> No grazing cattle through their prickly round
>   Can reach to wound ;
> But, as they grow where nothing is to fear,
> Smooth and unarm'd the pointless leaves appear."

In some places the young shoots are gathered by the peasants, dried, bruised, and used as a winter cattle-food. No doubt, in the early history of the Holly, cattle found out its good qualities for themselves, and browsed upon the then-unarmed foliage. In self-defence the tree developed spines upon its leaves, and so kept its enemies at a respectful distance. Above the reach of these marauders the production of spines would be a useless waste of material.

The flowers of the Holly, though small, are conspicuous by their great number and white colour. They are about a quarter

Flowers of Holly.

Pl. 82.

Fruits of Holly.

Pl. 83.

Pl. 84.

Bole of Holly.

Pl. 85.   *M* 87.

Spindle—winter.

of an inch across, with four petals and four stamens or stigmas. Sometimes flowers with stamens are produced by the same tree that bears flowers with stigmas ; but often the male and the female flowers are borne by separate trees, so that the possessor of a Holly that is solely male is sometimes puzzled by the fact that his tree, though covered with blossom, never produces a berry. The fruit is analogous in structure to that of the Plum and Cherry, and is technically termed a *drupe ;* but instead of the single stone of these fruits, in the Holly-berry there are four bony little stones, each with its contained seed. The berries ripen about September, and are then scarlet and glossy, though here and there one finds a tree whose fruit never gets beyond the yellow stage of coloration.

Most parts of the tree have had their uses in medicine ; the leaves, for example, being said to have value as a febrifuge, and the berries as a purgative, or in large doses (6 to 8) as an emetic. The smooth bark of large Hollies is often attacked by one of the most striking of our native lichens—*Graphis elegans*—whose black fruiting portions look like a raised cunei-form inscription. The Holly is not greatly subject to the attacks of insects, but many of its leaves will be found to have been tunnelled between the upper and lower skins by the larva of a minute moth, one of the Leaf-miners. It also provides the pabulum for the caterpillar of the Holly-blue butterfly (*Lycæna argiolus*). The dead leaves may be examined for the minute Prickly Snail (*Helix aculeata*).

The wood of the Holly has an exceedingly fine grain, due to its slow growth, and it is very hard and white. These qualities make it valuable for many purposes, often as a substitute for Box-wood and, when dyed black, in lieu of Ebony.

M

The Spindle-tree (*Euonymus europæus*).

The Spindle is right on the borderland between trees and shrubs, for though it will grow into a tree twenty feet high, yet our hedgerow specimens are usually bushlike, and only ten or twelve feet high. Until the autumn the Spindle, we fear, is rarely recognized as such, but gets confused with Buckthorn and Dogwood. In October, however, its quaint fruits have changed to a pale crimson hue, which renders them the most conspicuous feature of a hedgerow—even of one plentifully decorated with scarlet hips and haws and bryony-berries. The unusual tint of the Spindle, and the fact that it swings on a slender stalk, at once mark it out from the rigid-stalked hips and haws.

The trunk of the Spindle is clothed in smooth grey bark. The twigs, which are in pairs, starting from opposite sides of a branch, are four-angled. The shining leaves vary from egg-shaped to lance-shaped, with finely-toothed edges. They are arranged in pairs, and in autumn they change to yellow and red. When bruised they give off a fœtid odour, the juice is acrid, and said to be poisonous—a charge which is laid against the bark, flowers, and seed as well. The small greenish-white flowers are borne in loose clusters, of the type known as cymes, from the axils of the leaves, and appear in May and June. Some contain both stamens and pistil, but others are either stamenate *or* pistillate. The calyx is cut into four or six parts, the petals and stamens agree with these parts in number, but the lobes of the stigma only range from three to five, corresponding with the cells of the ovary. The fruit is deeply lobed, and marked with grooves, indicating the lines of future division, when the lobes open and disclose the seeds, at first covered with their orange jackets, or *arils*, after the manner of the mace that encloses the nutmeg.

Pl. 86.

Flowers of Spindle.

Pl. 87.

Fruits of Spindle-tree.

The hardness and toughness of Spindle-wood has long been esteemed in the fashioning of small wares where these qualities are essential, and the common name is a survival of the days when spinning was the occupation of every woman. Then spindles were in demand for winding the spun thread upon, and

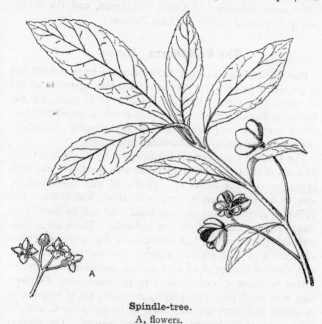

Spindle-tree.
A, flowers.

no wood was more suitable than that of Euonymus for making them. It shares with the Cornel (*Cornus sanguinea*) the name Dogwood; it is also Skewerwood, Prickwood, and Pegwood, all suggestive of uses to which it is or was applied. The young shoots make a very fine charcoal for artists' use.

The Spindle is indigenous throughout our islands, but cannot be said to be generally common ; it is rarer in Scotland and Ireland than in England.

Among the exotic species cultivated in our parks and gardens are the handsome variegated forms of the Evergreen Spindle (*Euonymus japonicus*) of China and Japan, and the Broad-leaved Spindle (*E. latifolius*) from Europe.

The Buckthorns (*Rhamnus*).

Our two native species of Buckthorn are trees of from five to ten feet in height. In this one respect they agree ; in almost all others they differ. Both are Buckthorns in name, but the Breaking Buckthorn (*Rhamnus frangula*) is quite unarmed, whilst many of the branchlets of the Purging Buckthorn (*Rhamnus catharticus*) are hardened into spines.

The Purging Buckthorn is distinguished by its stiff habit, and by some of the leaves being gathered into bundles at the ends of the shoots. The leaves are egg-shaped, with toothed edges, and of a yellowish-green tint, with short leaf-stalks. The yellowish-green flowers are very small, and will be found both singly and in clusters from the leaf-axils. There are a four-cleft calyx, four petals, four stamens, or four stigmas, for the sexes are usually on separate plants. The fruit is black, round, and about a quarter of an inch across, containing four stones. These so-called "berries" are ripe in September. Formerly they were much used as a purging medicine, but of so violent a character that their use has come to be discouraged, and the safer syrup of Buckthorn is prescribed instead. The juice of these berries is the raw material from which the artist's sap-green is prepared. It may be found in woods, thick hedgerows, and bushy places on commons southward of Westmoreland, showing a decided preference for chalky soils. In Ireland it only occurs rarely.

Pl. 88.

Breaking Buckthorn.

Pl. 89.

Fruits of Purging Buckthorn.

Pl. 90.

Unripe Fruits of Breaking Buckthorn.

Pl. 91.

Flowers of Wild Plum.

The Breaking Buckthorn (*Rhamnus frangula*) is also known as the Berry-bearing Alder, its leaves, with their lateral veins, presenting something of the appearance of the Alder. Its more slender stems are purplish-brown in hue, and *all* the leaves are arranged alternately up the stems. The leaves further differ from those of *R. catharticus* in having plain, un-

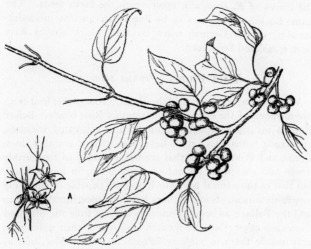

Purging Buckthorn.
A, flowers.

toothed edges, and their veins parallel one to another. The flowers are similar in size to those of the other species, but are whiter, less yellow, fewer in number, and on longer stalks. The parts of the flower, too, are in fives instead of fours ; and the "berry," though similar to the previous species, is much larger (half-inch diameter). In an unripe condition these fruits yield a good green dye, much used by calico printers and others. The wood made into charcoal is said to be the best for the purposes of the gunpowder makers, who know it by the name of Black Dogwood. The straight shoots of both species are used for forming walking and umbrella sticks, and those of longer growth for pea and bean sticks.

The Brimstone butterfly (*Gonepteryx rhamni*) lays its eggs on the leaves of *R. frangula*, upon which the larva feeds. The name Buckthorn appears to be due to an ancient misunderstanding of the German name Buxdorn, which should have been translated Box-thorn.

Wild Plums (*Prunus spinosa*).

With the single exception of the Hazel, all our native fruit-trees are members of the extensive and beautiful Rose family. Before Roman invasions brought improved and cultivated varieties, our "rude forefathers" must have been glad to eat the Sloes, Crabs, and Wild Cherries that are now regarded as too terribly crude and austere, in an uncooked condition, for any stomach but that of the natural boy, which appears capable of surviving any ill-treatment. Some authors have regarded the Wild Plum and the Bullace as being specifically distinct from the Sloe and from each other ; but the modern view is that their differences only entitle them to rank as sub-species of the Sloe, and as such they will be regarded here.

The Sloe or Blackthorn (*Prunus spinosa*) is the rigid many-branched shrub, with stiletto-like tips, that luxuriates on some of our commons and in our hedgerows. The blackish bark that gives its name to the shrub forms a fine foil in March or April for the pure white starry blossoms that brave the cold blasts before the leaf-buds dare unfurl their coverings. In some places—as in Cornwall, where it is the principal hedge plant, and where cliffs, creeks, and river banks are bordered by it— these bare black or purple stems are almost hidden by the

Pl. 92.

Sloes.

Pl. 93.

Blackthorn—spring.

abundant growth of the Grey Lichen (*Evernia prunastri*). In this, the typical form, the branches and twigs turn in every direction, so that it is impossible to thrust one's hand into a Blackthorn bush without getting considerably scratched. The well-known flower consists of a five-lobed calyx, five white petals,

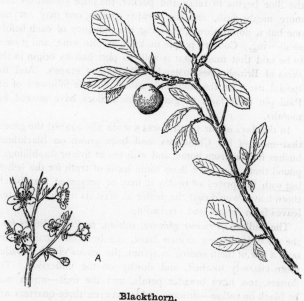

Blackthorn.
A, flowers.

and from fifteen to twenty stamens round the single carpel. The stigma matures in advance of the stamens, so that it has usually been fertilized by bee-borne pollen from another Sloe before its own anthers have disclosed their pollen. The fruit is about half an inch across, globose in form, and held erect upon its short stalk; black, but its blackness hidden by a delicate "bloom" that gives it a purplish glaucous hue. Terribly harsh are these fruits to the palate, and a mere bite at an unripe one is sufficient to set teeth on edge and contract the muscles of mouth and face. And yet, when the tight jacket of the Sloe begins to relax and pucker, the juice condenses into more mealy flesh, and the acridity passes, one may *eat* not one but a dozen, slowly, enjoying the piquancy of each before swallowing. Country people make them into wine, and it used to be said that much that is sold as port had its origin in the skins of British sloes instead of Portuguese grapes. And for special use "for the stomach's sake" old-wife followers of St. Paul pin their faith to gin in which Sloes have soaked for months.

In the days of our youth it was a stock jibe against the grocer that most of his China tea had been grown on Blackthorn bushes not far from home, and with tea at five or six shillings a pound there may have been some basis of truth for the belief; but with the prices of to-day it may be presumed that Blackthorn leaves would cost the dealer at least as much as real tea-leaves from Assam and Darjeeling.

The Bullace (*Prunus spinosa*, sub-sp. *insititia*) differs from the Sloe in having *brown* bark, the branches *straight* and only a few of them ending in spines, the leaves larger, broader, more coarsely toothed, and downy on the underside. The flowers, too, have broader petals, and the fruit—which may be black or yellow—droops, and is between three-quarters and one inch in diameter. In many places where this grows it can only be regarded as an escape from cultivation.

The Wild Plum (*Prunus spinosa*, sub-sp. *domestica*) has also brown bark, its branches straight, and not ending in spines. The downiness noticed on the underside of the Bullace leaves is here restricted to the ribs of the leaf. The fruit attains a diameter of an inch or an inch and a half. Although found

Pl. 94.

Gean in flower.

Flowers of Gean.

Pl. 95

occasionally in hedgerows, this sub-species is not indigenous in any part of our islands. Hooker says the only country in which it is really indigenous is Western Asia ; but its numerous cultivated forms are widely distributed.

It should be noted that the fruits of the Blackthorn and its sub-species are formed within the flower ; so are those of the Cherries, to be next described, the ovary being botanically termed "superior," that is, above the base of the calyx and corolla, when the flower is in an erect position. This is a point of some importance when one seeks to understand the different formation of the fruit in so closely related a species as the Apple, in which the ovary is "inferior," or below the flower.

Wild Cherries (*Prunus*).

Nature has been comparatively lavish in the matter of Cherries, for she has bestowed three species upon the British Islands. For the cultivated Cherry it is said that we ought to thank the Romans, as for many other good things in the way of food. Pliny states that we had the Cherry in Britain by the middle of the first century A.D. Evelyn tells us that the Cherry orchards of Kent owe their origin to "the plain industry of one Richard Haines, a printer to Henry VIII.," by whom "the fields and environs of about thirty towns, in Kent only, were planted with fruit trees from Flanders, to the unusual benefit and general improvement of the county to this day." It is probable, however, that our own countrymen had already effected some improvement on the wild sorts by cultivation, for even in the woods some trees are found bearing fruit much larger and of better flavour than usual, and such would be selected for cultivation.

Our three natives are the Wild or Dwarf Cherry (*Prunus cerasus*), the Gean (*P. avium*), and the Bird Cherry (*P. padus*).

N

Of these the Gean is the species most widely distributed throughout our country, and we therefore give it precedence.

The Gean (*Prunus avium*) is a tree that in suitable soils attains a height of thirty or forty feet, with short, stout branches, that take an upward direction. The leaves are large, broadly

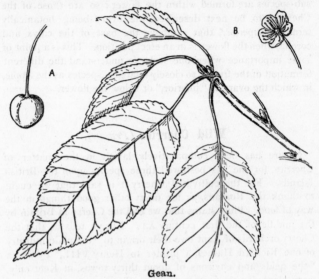

Gean.

A, fruit ; B, flower.

oval, with sharp-toothed edges, and downy on the underside. They always droop from the branches, and in spring they are of a bronzy-brown tint, which afterwards changes to pale green. Soon after the leaves have unfolded they are almost hidden by the umbels of wide-open white flowers, which have soft, heart-shaped petals, and whose anthers and stigmas mature simultaneously. The firm-fleshed drupe is heart-shaped, black

Pl. 96.   *N* 96.

Bird Cherry—spring.

Pl. 97.

Bole of Bird Cherry

or red, sweet or bitter, with scanty juice which stains the fingers. This is believed to be the original wild stock from which our modern Black Hearts and Bigarreau Cherries have been evolved by the cultivator.

The Dwarf or Wild Cherry (*Prunus cerasus*) is more bush-like than tree-like, for it sends up a great number of suckers

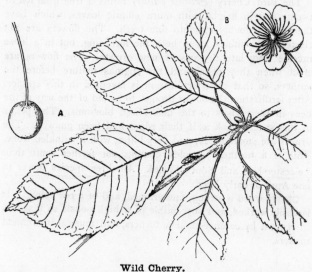

Wild Cherry.
A, fruit ; B, flower.

around the main stem. The branches are slender and drooping. The leaves, which are of similar shape to those of *P. avium*, are smooth and deep blue-green in tint, with round-toothed edges. The flowers are not so widely open as in the previous species, but retain more of the cup-shape, whilst the notched petals are firmer in consistence and oval in shape. The drupe is in this species round, with red skin and juicy flesh of a distinctly acid character. The juice does not stain as does that of *P. avium.* The Morello or Brandy Cherry, the May Duke, and the Kentish Cherries are considered to be derived from this species. This does not extend further north than Yorkshire ; in Ireland it is rare.

The Bird Cherry (*Prunus padus*) forms a tree from ten to twenty feet in height, with more elliptic leaves, which have their edges doubly cut into fine teeth. The flowers are not clustered in umbels, as in both the foregoing, but in a loose raceme from lateral spurs of new growth. The flowers are erect when they open, and the stigmas mature before the anthers, so that cross-fertilization is favoured in this species. After fertilization the flower droops, to be out of the way of the bees in their visits to the unfertilized blossoms. The petals in this species look as if their edges had been gnawed. The drupes are small, black, and very bitter, with a wrinkled stone. This is a northern species, coming not further south than Leicestershire and South Wales. All three species flower in late April or early May.

Cherry wood is strong, fine-grained, and of a red colour. It is easily worked, and susceptible of a high polish, so that it is in request by cabinet-makers, turners, and musical instrument makers.

The Wild Pear (*Pyrus communis*).

The Wild Pear is only to be found growing in the southern half of Britain, its northward range not extending beyond Yorkshire, and even in the south its claim to be regarded as a true native has been contested. Mr. Hewett C. Watson regards it as more probably a denizen, that is, a species originally introduced by man, which has maintained its hold upon the

Pl. 98.

Flowers of Wild Apple.

Pl. 99.

Bird Cherry—winter.

Pl. 100.

Wild Pear—spring.

Wild Apples.

Pl. 101.

new land.   Upon this assumption it is probable that the introduced specimens were already somewhat cultivated, but when
they (or their descendants) became wild they reverted to the
original condition of the species.

The Wild Pear, or Choke-pear, is a small tree, from twenty
to sixty feet in height, of somewhat pyramidal form. The twigs,

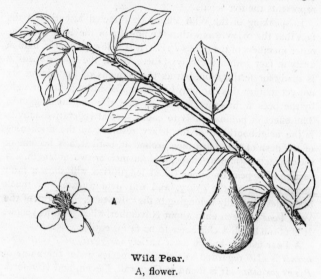

Wild Pear.
A, flower.

which are usually of a drooping tendency, are also much given
to ending in spines—a character scarcely apparent in the
cultivated tree. The leaves, too, of the wild tree are more
distinctly toothed than those of the Garden Pear. They are
oval in shape, with blunt-toothed edges, and downy on the
lower surface. Along the new shoots the leaves are arranged
alternately on opposite sides, but on shoots a year old they are

produced in clusters. The flowers, which measure more than an inch across, are pure white in colour, and are clustered in cymes of five to nine. They appear in April and May, and are of the Wild Rose type, there being numerous stamens, from three to five styles, which ripen before the stamens, five petals, and the calyx, taking the form of a pitcher with a five-lobed mouth, represents the five sepals.

In speaking of the Wild Plums we directed attention to the fact that the ovary was within the flower; in the Pear (and the other members of the genus *Pyrus*) it is below the flower, hidden away in fact within the calyx-tube. When the flower opens it is ready for fertilization, but as the stamens of that flower are not yet mature this can only be accomplished by pollen brought by the bees from other flowers as they rifle the honey-glands. The effect of pollination is to cause special vegetative activity in the neighbourhood of the ovary, resulting in the thickening of the flesh of the calyx-tube around it, until it has become of the characteristic pear-shape, and an inch or two in length. A section of a pear or apple, taken lengthwise, will show a faint green outline of the ovary, and will demonstrate how much of the flesh is really belonging to the calyx-tube. The fruit of the Wild Pear is green until about November, when it turns yellow. It is of too harsh a character to be fit for eating.

A Pear usually known as a variety (*briggsii*) of *Pyrus communis* is also regarded as a distinct species under the name of *Pyrus cordata*. It is found in Cornwall, Devon, and Hereford. Its more oval leaves are heart-shaped at the base, and its much smaller fruits often globular in form.

The Pear is a long-lived tree, that grows singly or in small groups on dry plains. It attains a height of about fifty feet in thirty years, and its girth may then be three or four feet. The timber is fine-grained, strong and heavy, with a reddish tinge. Stained with black, it is used to counterfeit ebony.

Pl. 102.

Bole of Wild Pear.

Wild Pear—winter.

The Wild Apple (*Pyrus malus*).

It is by no means an easy matter to decide whether the Crab-trees that grow along the hedgerows are truly wild or the offspring of orchard apples. In woods, away from gardens and orchards, there is less difficulty. Like the Pear, the Apple appears to have been the subject of cultural attention from very early times. This is proved by the philologists from the similarity of the equivalents for our word Apple in all the Celtic and Sclavonian languages, showing by their common origin that the fruit was of sufficient importance to have a distinctive name long before the separation of the peoples of Northern Europe. The name of Crab is of comparatively recent origin. Prior regards it as a form of the Lowland Scotch *scrab*, derived from Anglo-Saxon *scrobb*, a shrub, indicating that it is an Apple-bush rather than an Apple-tree.

The Wild Apple has not the pyramidal form of the Wild Pear, the branches spreading more widely when young and drooping when older, so that the head is rounded. In height it varies as a tree from twenty to thirty feet, though many examples of good age still retain the dimensions of a bush. Owing to the spreading character of the branches, the diameter of the head often exceeds the height of the tree. The bole has seldom any pretensions to symmetry, and is usually more or less crooked like the older branches. The brown bark is not very rough, though its numerous fissures and cracks give it a rugged appearance. Its wood, like that of the Pear, is hard and fine-grained, but, instead of having a reddish tinge, there is a tendency to brownness. The leaves vary in shape, but are more or less oblong, smooth above, sometimes downy on the lower surface when young, and with toothed edges.

The flowers are about the same size as those of the Wild Pear, but their white petals are beautifully tinted and streaked with pink. The small clusters are umbels—that is to say, the foot-stalks of similar length start from a common base. The fruit is almost spherical, and instead of the foot-stalk gradually merging into the apple, the attachment is always in a depression of the latter. In the typical form of the Wild Apple the yellow and

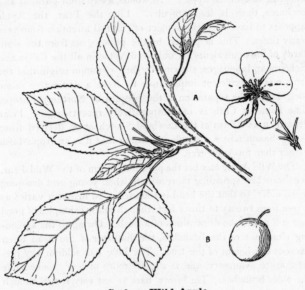

Crab or Wild Apple.
A, flower ; B, fruit.

red fruit hang by their slender stalks, but there is a variety (*mitis*) in which the fruit is borne *above* the stouter stalks. The variety may also be known by the downiness of the young leaves, the calyx-tube, and the stalks. The fruit is about an inch across, and so rich in malic acid as to be unfit for food in its natural

Wild Apple——summer.

Pl. 104.

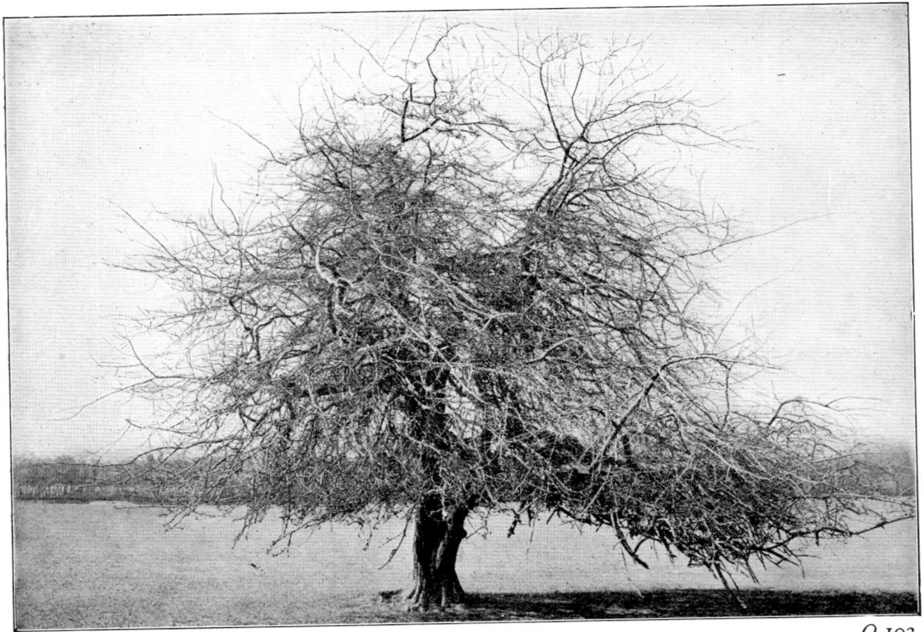

Wild Apple—winter.

Pl. 105.

state, though children punish their digestive organs with it. Pigs are partial to Crab-apples, a taste they have evidently inherited from the wild boar. A delicious preserve, called Crab-jelly, is made by stewing the whole fruit, then pressing the soft flesh through a hair sieve, and boiling the pulp with sugar. Cyder is made from the rotting Crabs ; also a kind of vinegar called verjuice, or vargis.

The Wild Apple is found all over the United Kingdom as far north as the Clyde, and wherever it is known to occur it is worth a special visit in May, when all its crooked branches and straggling shoots are rendered beautiful by the abundance of delicately tinted and fragrant flowers. It is also far from being unattractive in the autumn, when the miniature apples hang from the boughs.

White Beam (*Pyrus aria*).

Owing to its very local occurrence, the White Beam, though widely distributed, is one of the less known of our trees and shrubs. It comes into both these categories according to the situation of its growth, for whilst in exposed mountainous localities a specimen of mature age may be no more than four or five feet high, and of bush-like growth, under the lee of a wood, and on a calcareous soil, it will be an erect and graceful tree of pyramidal form, whose apex is forty feet from the ground. In its early years growth is tolerably rapid, but at the age of ten it slackens pace, and after it has attained its majority its progress is very slow. Its wood is fine-grained, very hard, white, but inclining to yellow. The bark is smooth, and little subject to the cracks and fissures that mark the Apple-bark. The branches, except a few of the lowest, all have an upward tendency.

The leaves vary considerably in the several forms or sub-species, but in the typical form they are a broad oval, with the edges

o

coarsely toothed or cut into lobes, the upper side smooth, and the lower side clothed with white cottony down, the almost straight nerves strongly marked. The white flowers, which appear in May or June, are only half an inch across, and gathered into loose clusters. They are succeeded by nearly round scarlet fruits, half

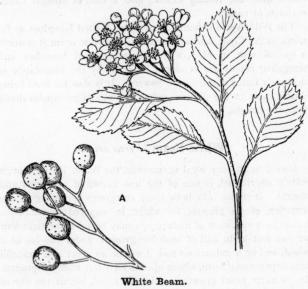

White Beam.

A, fruits.

an inch in diameter, known in Lancashire and Westmoreland as Chess-apples. The tree is also known in the same districts as Sea Owler, the latter word, according to Prior, being a corruption of Aller or Alder, probably from the resemblance of the leaves to those of *Alnus rotundifolia.* These Chess-apples are very sharp and rough to the taste, but when kept

Pl. 106.

Bole of Crab, or Wild Apple.

Pl. 107.

White Beam—spring.

like Medlars, till they "blet" or begin to decay, are far from unpleasant. Birds and squirrels eagerly seek for them on the tree, and those that fall are as welcome to hedgehogs and other mammals. This form is only found from the Midlands to the South of England as far west as Devon, and in Ireland.

The sub-species *latifolia* (*Pyrus rotundifolia* of some botanists) has broader leaves, varying from oval-oblong to almost round, divided into wedge-shaped lobes, the cottony down beneath being grey rather than white, and the nerves less prominent on the underside. This form is rare in hilly woods.

The sub-species *scandica* (also known as *Pyrus intermedia*) has the leaves less tough, more deeply divided into rounded or oblong lobes, and the grey cotton beneath of a looser character. This form is found in Scotland.

It should be noted that this species must not be called the White Beam-*tree*, for the word *beam* is the Saxon equivalent for tree. Other names for it include Hen-apple, Cumberland Hawthorn, Hoar Withy, Quick Beam, and Whipcrop.

THE WILD SERVICE (*Pyrus torminalis*) is a small tree of local occurrence, which does not extend farther north than Lancashire. In general appearance it may be taken for the White Beam, but closer inspection will reveal the following differences. The leaves, which are cut into tapering lobes and coarsely toothed, are heart-shaped at the base ; when young they are slightly downy beneath, but when mature they are smooth on both sides. Though the flowers are similar in size and colour to those of the White Beam, the fruit is smaller (one-third inch in diameter), less globular, and more like a large haw, though the colour is greenish-brown. The flowers appear in April and May, and the fruit, which is of a very dry, juiceless character, is ripe in November. In some localities these fruits are marketed, but they require to be kept like Medlars, until decay sets in, before they are fit to be eaten.

Mountain Ash, or Rowan (*Pyrus aucuparia*).

Little description of the Mountain Ash is needed, for in recent years it has come so much into favour that it is now one of the commonest of the trees planted in little suburban gardens and fore-courts. Its hardiness, its indifference to the character of the soil, the fact that other plants will grow beneath it, and the absence of need for pruning—all these points unite to make it suitable and popular for growth in restricted spaces. But the wood on the hillside is the natural home of the Mountain Ash, and in the Highlands its vertical range extends to 2600 feet above sea-level.

The Mountain Ash attains a height of from thirty to fifty feet, and has a straight clean bole, clothed in smooth grey bark, scarred horizontally as though it had been scored with a knife. All the branches have an upward tendency, and the shoots bear the long feathery leaves, whose division into six or eight pairs of slender leaflets suggests *the* Ash, from which part of its name has been borrowed. Gazing on this tree either in flower or fruit, it would be quite unnecessary to explain that it is not even remotely allied to *Fraxinus excelsior*, and that the similarity of leaf-division is the only point of resemblance between them. These leaflets have toothed edges, are paler on the underside, and in a young condition the midrib and nerves are hairy. The creamy-white fragrant flowers are like little Hawthorn blossoms, though only half the size, and they appear in dense clusters (*cymes*) in May or June. The fruit are miniature apples, of the size of holly-berries, bright scarlet without and yellow within. They ripen in September, and are then a great attraction to thrushes, blackbirds, and their kind, who rapidly strip the tree of them. Though this at first sight may appear like frustrating the tree's object in producing fruit, it is not really so, the attractive flesh being a mere bait to induce the birds to pass the seeds through their intestines, and thus

get them sown far and wide. By this method the process of
germination is considerably hastened, whereas by hand-sowing
the seeds lie in the earth for eighteen months before shooting.
All the species of *Pyrus* produce their fruits with this object,
the larger more or less brownish ones being intended to attract
mammals, the smaller and red-coloured to tempt birds. The

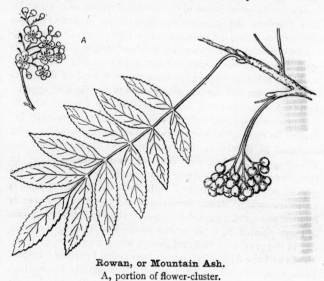

Rowan, or Mountain Ash.
A, portion of flower-cluster.

seeds have leathery jackets to protect them from the action of
the digestive fluids, and are further wrapped in a parchmenty,
bony, or wooden "core" (*endocarp*) with a similar object. In
the case of the Rowan this is very like wood.

In the south of Britain the Mountain Ash is chiefly grown as
underwood and used as a nurse for oaks and other timber trees,
which soon outgrow it and kill it; so that in the woods it is

seldom allowed to grow into a fully developed tree, but, thanks to the birds, it comes up on the common and the hillside, and has a chance of producing its masses of ruby fruit. Its wood is tough and elastic, but, owing to the smallness of its girth, it does not produce timber of any size. Still, it makes admirable poles and hoops.

The word Rowan is one of the most interesting of tree-names, and connects the still-existing superstitious practices of our northern counties, not only with the old Norsemen, but with the ancient Hindus who spoke the Sanskrit tongue. The word is spelled in many ways which connect it with the Old Norse *runa*, a charm, it being supposed to have power to ward off the effects of the evil eye. In earlier times *runa* was the Sanskrit appellation for a magician ; *rûn-stafas* were staves cut from the Rowan-tree upon which runes were inscribed. Until quite recently the respect for its magical properties was shown in the north by fixing a branch of Rowan to the cattle-byre as a charm against the evil designs of witches, warlocks, and others of that kidney. In this connection we may quote also from Evelyn's "Sylva." He says : " Ale and beer brewed with these berries, being ripe, is an incomparable drink, familiar in Wales, where this tree is reputed so sacred that there is not a churchyard without one of them planted in it (as among us the Yew) ; so, on a certain day in the year, everybody religiously wears a cross made of the wood ; and the tree is by some authors called Fraxinus Cambro-Britannica, reputed to be a preservative against fascinations and evil spirits ; whence, perhaps, we call it witchen, the boughs being stuck about the house or the wood used for walking-staves."

Among the numerous names of the Mountain Ash are Fowler's Service (or Servise, from *Cerevisia*, a fermented drink), Cock-drunks, Hen-drunks (from the belief that fowls were intoxicated by eating the "berries"), Quickbeam, White Ash (from the colour of the flowers), Witch-wood, and Witchen.

Pl. 112.

Bole of Rowan.

Pl. 113.

Flowers of Rowan.

Quickbeam is in allusion to the constant movement of foliage, quick being the Anglo-Saxon *cwic*, alive. Witch-wood and Witchen are also forms of *cwic*.

The True Service (*Pyrus sorbus*) closely resembles the Mountain Ash in habit and foliage, but it is not a native of Britain, though it used to be claimed as such, on account of its growing in the more mountainous parts of Cornwall and in Wyre Forest, Worcestershire. The latter, however, is the only Service tree that could put in such a claim, for it grows —or grew?—far from habitations or cultivated land, and the presumption is that it has not owed its introduction to man. Still, "one swallow does not make a summer," and a solitary wild tree does not give the species a title to be reckoned as British. It is occasionally cultivated here, and its portrait, with a brief account of its points of difference from the Mountain Ash, may be useful. A comparison of the photographs from the boles of the two species will show a great difference : that of the Mountain Ash being smooth, whilst that of the Service is rugged. The leaf is similarly broken up into paired leaflets, but these are broader, and are downy on both upper and lower sides. The white flowers are as large as May-blossoms, and the fruits, which may be either apple-shaped or pear-shaped, are greenish-brown, with rusty specks, and four times the size of Rowan-berries. In winter, when there are neither leaves, flowers, nor fruits to help in the distinction, the bark may be taken in conjunction with the leaf-buds, which are green and smooth in this species, whilst those of the Mountain Ash are black and downy. The fruit may be eaten after it has begun to decay, as in the case of the Medlar.

Loudon describes the wood of the Service as the hardest and heaviest of all the trees indigenous to Europe : fine-grained, red-tinted, susceptible of a high polish, and much in request in France for all purposes where strength and durability are needed. He further says that it takes two centuries to attain its full stature (fifty to sixty feet), "and lives to so great an age that some specimens of it are believed to be upwards of 1000 years old."

We have already made reference to the meaning of the name Service. Another name—Sorb (from Latin *sorbeo*)—shows closer affinity for the fermented liquor indicated by Servise, for it means "drink down." A third name is Chequer-tree, which Dr. Prior tells us is an antique pronunciation of the word *choker*, in allusion to the unpalatable fruit, fit to choke one. Choke-pear, it will be remembered, is a synonym of the Wild Pear. Britten and Holland regard the name Chequer-tree as having no connection with choking, but an indication of the chequered or spotted appearance of the fruit.

The Medlar (*Pyrus germanica*) is a small tree, native of Persia, Asia Minor, and Greece, but which is generally held to occur wild in England and the Channel Islands only as an escape from cultivation. The theory is that the tree was introduced at some date prior to 1596—when we have record of its being in cultivation here—and that the Medlar-trees growing in the hedges of south and middle England are from seeds of these cultivated trees, which have been sown by birds, or more probably mammals who have eaten the fruit. The fact that it is not found in woods is taken as evidence that it is non-indigenous. Such evidence is not the most convincing, but it is the best available. It should be noted, however, that the agents credited with its distribution along our hedgerows have free access to woods, and that if these places were favourable to the growth of the Medlar, we should probably find it there, whether indigenous or exotic. Much more conclusive, we think, is its restricted distribution abroad, as already indicated. One would not expect to find a tree whose nearest home is Greece,

Pl. 114.

Rowan—winter.

Pl. 117.

C 111.

Bole of True Service.

leaping over the whole of Europe and appearing as an indigene in Britain.

In its wild condition the Medlar is a much-branched and spiny tree, from ten to twenty feet high, in these respects resembling the Hawthorn; but, like the Pear, it puts off its

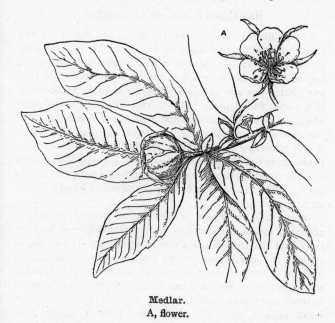

Medlar.
A, flower.

defences when cultivated. Its leaves are large and undivided, of an oblong-lance shape, downy beneath, and sometimes with the edges very finely toothed. The solitary white flowers are large—one and a half inches across—with a woolly calyx, whose five tips expand into leafy growths. They appear in May or

June, and are succeeded by brown fruits, an inch or less across, which may be described as round, with a depressed top, which is ornamented with the remains of the calyx-lobes. They ripen in October or November.

Hawthorn (*Cratægus oxyacantha*).

Though distributed as a wild tree throughout the length and breadth of the British Islands, we are all more familiar with the Hawthorn as planted material in the construction of hedges, and this is a use to which it has been put ever since land was plotted out and enclosed. For the word is Anglo-Saxon (*hægthorn*), and signifies hedge-thorn. The man in the street would say without hesitation that Hawthorn means the thorn that produces Haws, but the philologist would tell him that it is only a modern and erroneous practice to apply the name of the hedge to the fruit of the hedge-thorn. It is also Whitethorn, to make the distinction between its light-grey bark and that of the Blackthorn; and May because of the period when it chiefly attracts attention.

Where the Hawthorn is allowed its natural growth, it attains a height of forty feet, with a circumference between three and ten feet. Such a tree is represented in our photograph. On our commons, where in their youth the Hawthorns have to submit to much mutilation from browsing animals, their growth is spoiled; but though some of these never become more than bushes tangled up with Blackthorn into small thickets, there are others that form a distinct bole and a round head of branches from ten to twenty feet high, which in late May or (more frequently) early June look like solid masses of snow. The characteristic of the tree which makes it so valuable as fencing material is found in its numerous branches, supporting a network of twigs so dense that even a hand may not be pushed among them without

Pl. 118.

P. 112.

Fruits of Hawthorn.

Pl. 123.

Hawthorn—winter.

have been fertilized the corollas drop off, so that in the flowering season (September and October) the ground beneath will usually be found strewn with them. The fruit is a round berry, of an orange-red hue, whose surface is completely

Strawberry-tree.

studded with little points. As these berries do not come to maturity until about fourteen months after the flowers have dropped their corollas, we may see both flowers and almost full-formed fruit on the tree at the same time. They are not eatable until quite ripe, and even then they are not to everybody's taste, on account of their austerity. In truth, we have it on the testimony of Pliny that the old Latin name *unedo*, now enshrined in the specific scientific name, was given to it because to eat one of these tree strawberries was a sufficiently extensive acquaintance for most persons.

It is perhaps unnecessary to add that, in spite of the name, there is no relationship existing between this tree and *the* Strawberry; nor is there more than a faint superficial resemblance between the fruits of the two plants. The Strawberry belongs to the great Rose family, whilst the nearest British connections of the Arbutus are the Bilberries and Heaths.

Dogwood (*Cornus sanguinea*).

Among the constituents of the broad hedgerow, and the copse that borders many a country road, the Dogwood or Cornel is apt to be overlooked as Privet, to which its similar, opposite leaves and clusters of small white flowers bear a superficial resemblance. It has a great variety of local names, though it must be admitted that many of these show close connections one with another. This, however, makes them not less interesting, but indicates how ancient and general is the underlying idea which has given rise to them. Dogwood had originally no connection with dogs, but was the wood of which dags, goads, and skewers were made, because, as the Latin *Cornus* signifies, it was of horny hardness and toughness. When the etymology got changed by the substitution of " o " for " a " in dag, it was also called Dog-tree, Dog-berry, Dog-timber, and Houndberry-tree, and to explain the name it was said that the bark made an excellent wash for mangy dogs. Gatter, Gatten, Gaiter, Gaitre-berry, are all from the Anglo-Saxon *Gad-treow*, or goad-tree;

Strawberry Tree.

Pl. 125.

Fruits of Dogwood.

Gadrise means Goad-shrub (*Gad-riis*), and Gatteridge is *gaitre rouge*, from the red colour of the bare twigs.

But we must not overlook the shrub itself whilst considering its wealth of names. It grows to a height of six or eight feet, and is clothed with opposite oval leaves, which are smooth on

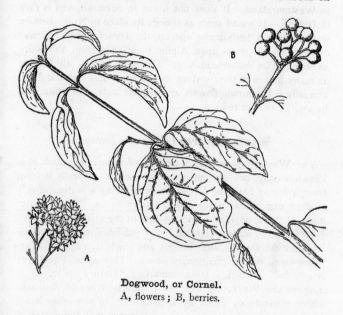

Dogwood, or Cornel.
A, flowers ; B, berries.

both surfaces. The honeyed flowers are produced in June or July at the extremities of the branches in dense round cymes. Individually they are small (one-third of an inch across), opaque white, with four petals and four stamens ; the central flower, which opens first, has five petals and stamens. Their unpleasant odour appears to render them more attractive to flies and small beetles. The flowers are succeeded by small green berries, which turn purple-black about September, and are exceedingly bitter. They are said to yield an oil which is used in France for soap-making, and has been here burned in lamps.

The Dogwood is widely distributed over Britain as far north as Westmoreland. It does not occur in Scotland, and is rare in Ireland. It would seem as though its place in North Britain was taken by a herbaceous species, the Dwarf Cornel (*Cornus suecica*), which grows upon Alpine moorlands from Yorkshire as far north as Sutherlandshire. The stems of this, which have as many inches to their stature as the shrub has feet, die down annually. Its minute flowers are purplish instead of white, and its smaller berries red.

Wayfaring-tree (*Viburnum lantana*).

The Wayfaring-tree has a number of names by which it is known locally, but the one we have used is generally known, though it may have the disadvantage of being a comparatively modern one whose parentage is known to us. The origin of most of these popular names is lost in the mists of antiquity. John Gerarde, whose "Herbal" was published in 1597, noting its fondness for roadside hedges and thickets, called it Wayfaring-tree, or Wayfaringman's-tree. Thereupon Parkinson, nearly half a century later, remarks: "Gerard calleth it in English the Wayfaring tree, but I know no travailer doth take either pleasure or profit by it more than by any other hedge trees." Our own experience serves to prove that Wayfarers, as a class, have improved since Parkinson's day, for we have frequently been questioned in the Surrey chalk-districts, at various seasons, respecting the bold plant; in winter showing its large naked buds, all rough with starry hairs, which keep off frost, as well as do the many scales and thick varnish of Horse-chestnut buds; in summer the broad, hairy leaves, looking

Pl. 126.

Flowers of Dogwood.

Pl. 127.

Fruits of Wayfaring-tree.

as dusty as a miller's coat, whilst above them spread the slightly rounded heads of white flowers; later, when the flowers are succeeded by bunches of glowing coral beads, that in autumn become beads of jet. It is not confined to the chalk-hills, but as far north as Yorkshire may be looked for wherever the soil is

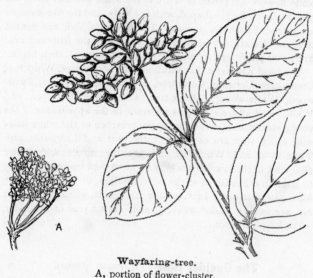

Wayfaring-tree.
A, portion of flower-cluster.

dry, though it finds this condition best on the chalk, and is there especially abundant. It is not indigenous in either Scotland or Ireland.

Though it grows to a height of twenty feet in places, it can never properly be called a tree. Its downy stems are never very stout. They branch a good deal, and it should be noted that the branches are always given off in pairs, a branch from

Q

each side of the stem at exactly the same height; the leaves are produced in the same order. These leaves, which are three or four inches in length, are much wrinkled, heart-shaped, with a blunt, small end, white beneath, and the edges very finely toothed. The flower-cluster is a cyme, and it should be noted that all the white flowers comprised in it are of the same size and form, the corollas being funnel-shaped, with five lobes, and the five stamens are extruded from the mouth. The flowers, which are jointed to the stalks, are out in May and June, and the flattened oval fruits that follow are, as already stated, at first red, then black.

The local names for this shrub include Mealy-tree, Whipcrop, Cotton-tree, Cottoner, Coventree, Lithe-wort, Lithy-tree, Twist-wood, White-wood. Mealy-tree, Cotton-tree, Cottoner, and White-wood all have obvious reference to the appearance of the young shoots and leaves, due to the presence of the white hairs with which they are covered. Lithe-wort and Lithy-tree, also Twist-wood and Whipcrop, indicate the supple and elastic character of the branches, which are often used instead of Withy to bind up a bundle of sticks or vegetables, or to make a hoop for a gate-fastener. In Germany the shoots, when only a year old, are used in basket-weaving, and, when a year or two older, serve for pipe-stems.

The Guelder Rose (*Viburnum opulus*).

Although the Guelder Rose and the Wayfaring-tree are very closely related, the differences between them are so great that there is little danger of any person with ordinary powers of observation confusing them. The Guelder Rose does not grow so tall as its congener, twelve feet being about the extreme height to which it attains in a wild state, and ordinarily it is several feet less. It is not so fond of dry soils, and is more frequently found in the copse, where it is not subject to the

Pl. 128.

Wayfaring Tree.

Pl. 129.

Q 121.

Elder.

extremes of heat and cold that have produced the hairy covering of *V. lantana*. The stems and branches are quite smooth,
and the leaf-buds are wrapped in scales. The young leaves,
it is true, when they break from the bud, are covered with

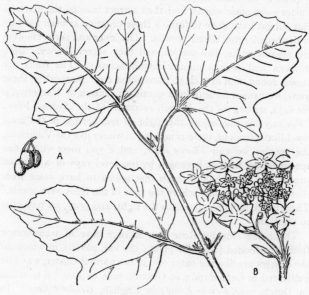

Guelder Rose.
A, fruit ; B, flowers.

down, but they throw this off as they expand to their full
size, and become smooth on either side. Instead of the leaf
being heart-shaped, it is divided into three deeply toothed
lobes, and it will be noted that at the base of the leaf-stalk
there is a pair of slender stipules, which *lantana* never has.

The cyme or flower-head is more rounded, and whilst the mass of flowers are of the same size (a quarter of an inch) as those of the Wayfaring-tree, those in the outer row are three times the size—but they are entirely without stamens or pistil! It would appear that in order to make the flower-cluster more conspicuous, and thus attract insects, the material that should have gone to furnish these organs has been used up in the broader and whiter corolla. The inner and perfect flowers are creamy-white, bell-shaped, and they secrete honey. Both stamens and stigma mature simultaneously. The fruits are almost round, and of a clear, translucent red. Respecting these fruits, we cannot forbear from quoting a remark of Hamerton's. He says, writing as the French recorder of the *Sylvan Year*: "For any one who enjoys the sight of red berries in the most jewel-like splendour, there is nothing in winter like the Viburnum, the species we call *Viorne obier*, and if you meet with a fine specimen just when it is caught by the level rays of a crimson sunset, you will behold a shrub that seems to have come from that garden of Aladdin where the fruit of the trees were jewels." These fruits, though enticing to the sight, and juicy, are nauseous to the taste.

The name Guelder Rose is a strange case of transference from a cultivated to a wild plant : the var. *sterilis*, in which *all* the flowers are like the outer row in the normal cluster, was first cultivated in Gelderland ; so Gerarde tells us that " it is called in Dutch, *Gheldersche Roose;* in English, *Gelder's Rose."* In the Cotswolds it is known as King's Crown, from the " King of the May" having been crowned with a chaplet of it. Another name for it is Water Elder, presumably given on account of the similar appearance of the flower-clusters in *Viburnum* and *Sambucus*.

The distribution of the Guelder Rose as a wild plant extends northwards to Caithness, although it is rare in Scotland. It occurs throughout Ireland.

Pl. 130.

Fruits of the Guelder Rose.

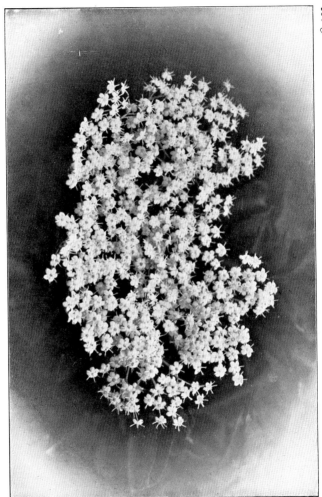

Flowers of Elder.

Pl. 131.

The Elder (*Sambucus nigra*).

The Elder is more a tree of the wayside than of the woodland, often of low bushy growth ; but where it finds good loamy soil with abundant moisture it attains a height of twenty feet.   None

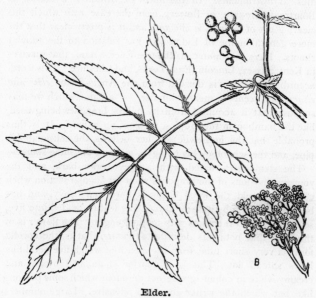

Elder.
A, berries ; B, portion of flower-cluster.

of our trees grows more rapidly in its earliest years, and any bit of its living wood will readily take root, so that its presence in the hedge is often due to planting for the purpose of rapidly erecting a live screen.   Its quickly grown juicy shoots soon harden into a tube of tough wood with a core of pith which is readily extracted, and renders the tube available for a pea-shooter, a pop-gun, or a music-pipe. Such uses have been known from remote antiquity—probably one might say from the beginnings of the human race. The ancient Greeks called it *Sambúke*, from its wood having been used in the making of musical instruments. In the north of Britain it is known as Bourtree, Bore-tree, or Bottery, from the ease with which this clearing out of the pith is effected, and it is pretty clear that the more general name of Elder also has relation to the tubular shoots. Piers Plowman calls the tree Eller, a name that survives in Kent, Sussex, Lincoln, East Yorks, and Cheshire. This word, according to Prior, is derived from the Anglo-Saxon *eller* and *ellarn*, and seems to mean " kindler "—" a name which we may suppose that it acquired from its hollow branches being used, like the bamboo in the tropics, to blow up a fire." It is thus probable that the housewife got her bellows, the musician his pipe, and the schoolboy his pop-gun, all from the same source.

The stems are coated with a grey corky bark, and the younger divisions of the branches show an angular section when cut. When old, the wood becomes hard and heavy, and has been used as a substitute for Box. The leaf is divided into five, seven, or nine oval leaflets with toothed edges. The flower is of the form that botanists describe as *rotate*, that is, the corolla forms a very short tube, from the mouth of which five petal-like lobes spread flat. This is a quarter of an inch broad, and creamy-white in colour, giving out an odour which some persons like, but which the writer considers offensive. Large numbers of these small flowers are gathered into flat-topped cymes, five or six inches in diameter. The primary stalks of these cymes are five in number. The flowers are succeeded by small globular berries, ultimately of a purple-black hue, and of mawkish flavour, which are yet much sought after by country people for the making of Elderberry wine, which they credit with marvellous medicinal powers. In truth, the Elder still retains among rustic folk much

Pl. 132.

Box Trees.

Pl. 133.

Bole of Box.

of the reputation it had when John Evelyn praised it so highly in his " Sylva," where he says, " If the medicinal properties of the leaves, bark, berries, etc., were thoroughly known, I cannot tell what our countryman could ail for which he might not fetch a remedy from every hedge, either for sickness or wound."

Occasionally one may find in the hedgerow an Elder with its leaflets deeply cut into very slender lobes, so that the leaf has resemblance to that of Fool's Parsley. This is an escape from cultivation—a garden variety (*laciniata*) known as the Cut-leaved or Parsley-leaved Elder.

The Box (*Buxus sempervirens*).

Though frequently to be met with in parks and ornamental grounds, there are only a few places in this country where the Box is really indigenous. These are in the counties of Surrey, Kent, Buckingham, and Gloucester. On the famous Box Hill, near Dorking, in Surrey, it may be seen attaining its proper proportions as a small tree, and in sufficient abundance to form groves covering a considerable area. It grows to a height of fifteen or twenty feet, with a girth of about twenty inches. Its slender branches are clothed with small, oblong, leathery leaves, which give out a peculiar and distinctive odour. They are about an inch in length, polished on the upper side, evergreen, and opposite.

The flowers may be looked for from January to May, and will be found clustered between the leaf and the stem. These are quite small and inconspicuous, of a whitish-green colour, and the sexes are in separate flowers. The uppermost one in the centre of each cluster is a female flower ; the others are males. The males consist of four petals, enclosing a rudimentary ovary, from beneath which spring four stamens. The sepals of the female flower vary in number, from four to twelve, and enclose a rounded ovary with three styles, which are ripe and protruded before the males open. This develops into the three-celled capsule with three diverging beaks, which correspond with the styles, and in each cell there are one or two black seeds.

The growth of the tree is very slow, and, in consequence, the

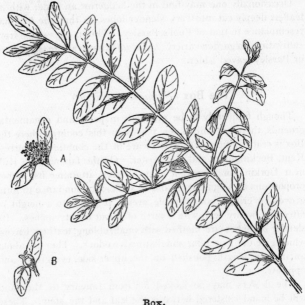

Box.

A, male flowers ; B, female flower.

grain of its wood is very fine. It is also very hard, and so heavy that alone among native woods it will not float in water. On account of its fine grain and hardness, it is in request by the turner and mathematical instrument maker, and was formerly largely used by the wood-engraver for "woodcuts." Since the introduction of the photographic "process" blocks, the industry of preparing Box-wood for the engraver must have become all but extinct, and for that reason Box plantations must be less valuable assets than formerly. It is on record that when the Box Hill trees were cut in 1815, the "fall" realized nearly £10,000. Box Hill is in no sense a plantation; its slopes and summit are clothed with a natural mixed wood of Box, Oak, Beech, and Yew. Beneath every Box-tree will be found hundreds of seedlings of various ages. Some of these may be seen in our photograph, which depicts naturally grown Box-trees on the famous hill. It will be noted that their "habit" is widely different from that of the more bush-like forms so familiar in gardens.

PART II.

EXOTIC TREES AND SHRUBS.

We have already given descriptions and illustrations of several exotic species in Part I., where it seemed more advantageous to the reader to include them with British species of the same genus ; those now to be dealt with are in all cases members of genera not represented in our native Flora.

The Plane (*Platanus acerifolia*).

In spite of the fact that the Plane is an exotic of comparatively recent introduction, it seems in a fair way of being associated in the future with London. It has taken with great kindness to London life, in spite of the drawbacks of smoke, fog, flagstones, and asphalt. Its leaves get thickly coated with soot, which also turns its light-grey bark to black ; but as the upper surface of the leaves is smooth and firm, a shower of rain washes them clean, and the rigid outer layer of bark is thrown off by the expansion of the softer bark beneath. This is not thrown off all at once, but in large and small flakes, which leave a smooth yellow patch behind, temporarily free from soot contamination. A variety of trees has been tried for street-planting, but none has stood the trying conditions of London so well as

Pl. 134.

Plane Tree—summer.

Pl. 135.

Bole of Plane Tree.

the Plane, and therefore before many years the capital will be
the city of Planes.

Two species are recognized—the Oriental Plane (*Platanus
orientalis*) and the Western Plane (*P. occidentalis*); but it
would probably be more accurate to regard them as geographical

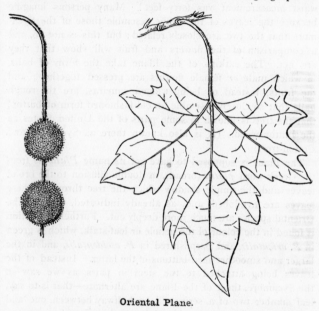

Oriental Plane.

varieties of one species, the points in which they differ being
small and not very important. Thus the leaves of the Oriental
Plane are described as being so much more deeply lobed than
those of the Western Plane that the former are botanically
described as palmate; but the two forms of leaf may often be
found on the same individual. The Western Plane, too, does

not shed its bark in small flakes like the Oriental Plane, but in large sheets.

Planes normally rise to a height of something between seventy and ninety feet, and the trunk attains a circumference of from nine to twelve feet ; but there is a record of a portly Plane whose waist measurement was forty feet ! Many persons imagine because the leaves of the Plane resemble those of the Sycamore that the two are closely related ; but this is not so, and a comparison of the flowers and fruit will show that they are not. The catkins of the Plane take the form of balls, in which male *or* female flowers are pressed together ; and the fruits, instead of being winged samaras, are the rough balls that so closely resemble an old-fashioned form of button, that the tree is known in some parts of the United States as the Button-wood. (It is also known there as Sycamore and Cotton-tree.)

The Plane is supposed to have got its name *Platanus* from the Greek word *platus* (broad), in double allusion to the broad leaves and the ample shadow which the tree throws. These leaves are five-lobed, and, as already indicated, those of the Oriental species are much more deeply cut. Further distinction is found in the colour of the petiole or leaf-stalk, which is green in *P. orientalis*, and purplish-red in *P. occidentalis*, and in the larger and smoother seed-buttons of the latter. Instead of the leaves being attached to the stem in pairs, as we saw in the Sycamore, those of the Plane are alternate—that is to say, leaf number two of a series will be halfway between one and three, but on the opposite side of the shoot.

The outline of the tree is not so regular as in most others, the leaves being gathered in heavy masses, with broad spaces between, rather than equally distributed over the head. This is, of course, due to the freedom with which the crooked arms are flung about. The pale-brown wood is fine-grained, tough, and hard, and is extensively used by pianoforte-makers, coachbuilders, and cabinet-makers, but is not highly esteemed for other purposes to which timber is put in this country.

The Oriental Plane is popularly supposed to have been introduced to England from the Levant by Francis Bacon, but if Loudon's statement that it was "in British gardens before 1548" rests on good evidence, Bacon's claim is dismissed, for *he* was not "introduced" until 1561. It is nearly a hundred years later (1640) that the Occidental Plane was first brought from Virginia by the younger Tradescant, and planted in that remarkable garden of his father's in South Lambeth Road. The form that has done so well in London is the Maple-leaved Plane (*Platanus acerifolia*), which we have chosen as the subject for our photographs. The leaves are less deeply divided than those of the Oriental Plane. It is believed to be a hybrid between the other two, and to have first appeared in the Oxford Botanic Garden about 1670. Some fine examples may be seen in London parks and squares. It is not known anywhere in the wild state.

The Walnut (*Juglans regia*).

In the Golden Age, when man lived happily on a handful of acorns, the gods fed upon walnuts, and so their name was *Jovis glans*—the nuts of Jupiter—since contracted into *Juglans*. Those who delight in obvious interpretations by appealing to the modern meanings of words similar in construction may be pardoned for supposing that Walnut-trees were formerly trained against walls ; but, like many other obvious interpretations, this is wide of the mark. Some have gone back to the Anglo-Saxons for help, and though the result arrived at is in all probability the correct one, it is almost certain that the Anglo-Saxons knew nothing of the matter, and would scarcely trouble to give a name to something they had never seen. The Walnut is a native of the Himalayas, the Hindu Kush, Persia, Lebanon, and

Asia Minor to Greece. The learned Roman, Varro, who was born B.C. 116, and died B.C. 28, mentions it as existing in Italy in his day ; and Pliny tells us it was brought thence from Persia. The date of its introduction to Britain is usually set down as about the middle of the sixteenth century, but it was probably at least a century earlier, for Gerarde, writing at the close of the sixteenth century, describes it as a tree commonly to be seen in orchards, and in fields near the highways, where a very new importation was not likely to be found. But to return to the name : there can be little doubt that it is a contraction of Wälsh-nut (in modern spelling, Welsh-nut), meaning foreign. This is German, and while the modern sons of the Vaterland write it Wallnuss (occasionally Wälshenuss), the Dutch form is Wallnoot. That this is the true derivation is made pretty certain by Gerarde, who calls it " Walnut, and of some Walsh-nut."

That the new importation was fully appreciated in Europe for its fruit may be judged by the extent to which its cultivation had spread in Evelyn's day, for he tells us the trees abounded in Burgundy, where they stood in the midst of goodly wheat-lands. He says : " In several places betwixt Hanau and Frankfort in Germany no young farmer is permitted to marry a wife till he bring proof that he hath planted and is a father of such a stated number of [Walnut] trees, and the law is inviolably observed to this day, for the extraordinary benefit the tree affords the inhabitants."

The Walnut is a handsome tree, growing to a height of forty to sixty feet, with a bole twenty feet or more in circumference, and a huge spreading head. The bark is of a cool grey colour, smooth when young, but as the tree matures deep longitudinal furrows form, and it becomes very rugged. The twisted branches take a direction more upward than horizontal, but in early summer they are almost completely hidden by the masses of large and handsome leaves of warm green colour and

Pl. 136.

Plane Tree—winter.

Walnut—summer.

Pl. 137.

spicy aroma. I once rejoiced in the occupation of a garden
that held two Walnut-trees, and though they had not attained
to the fruiting age, their possession was a delight to me; but
then I am one of those who enjoy their fragrance, which is un-

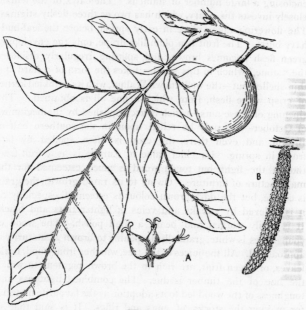

Walnut.

A, female flowers; B, male flowers.

bearable to some persons. The large leaves are formed after the
fashion of the Ash-leaf—broken up into a variable number of
lance-shaped leaflets with scarcely perceptible teeth.

The flowering of the Walnut is much on the plan of the Oak
and the Hazel, the sexes being in different flowers, but borne by

one tree ; the males forming a long drooping catkin of slender cylindrical form, the females being solitary, or a few grouped at the end of a shoot. Separated from the catkin, the males will each be seen to consist of a calyx of five greenish scales, enclosing a large number of stamens. The calyx of the female closely invests the ovary, which has two or three fleshy stigmas. The flowering takes place in early spring, before the leaf-buds have burst. The fruit is a plum-like drupe, only the enveloping green flesh becomes brown, and, splitting irregularly, discloses the "stone," which in this species takes the form of a hard but thin-shelled nut—the well-known Walnut, with its wrinkled kernel of crisp white flesh, from which a fine oil is obtained. The ripening of these nuts—which is accomplished by the beginning of October—can only be relied upon in the southern half of Britain, and even there the crop is often spoiled by late frosts in spring. Its chief value in Europe is as a fruit-tree, though the light but tough wood is much esteemed for the manufacture of furniture. Owing to its rapid growth, the grain is coarse, but the dark-brown colour is esteemed, especially as it is relieved by streaks and veins of lighter tints and black. It is easily worked, and bears a high polish. The wood of young trees is white, gradually deepening to brown as maturity is approached. All the juices of the tree, whether from wood, bark, leaves, or green fruit, are rich in the brown pigment to which the hue of the timber is due. The combined lightness and toughness of the wood led to its adoption as the favourite material for making the stocks of guns and rifles. It is said that so great was the demand for this purpose during the Peninsular War, that a single Walnut-tree realized £600 for its timber, and this created a boom that led to the cutting down of all our finest Walnut-trees. Some of these were doubtless the very trees referred to by Evelyn, who tells us the Walnut was extensively planted at Leatherhead in Surrey, also at Cassaulton (Carshalton) and Godstone in the same county, where the rambler may

Pl. 138.

Fruit of Walnut.

Walnut—winter.

Pl. 139.

come across fine Walnut-trees to this day, and occasionally to young ones growing wild in hedgerows and wastes.

The old doggerel adage, "A dog and a wife and a walnut-tree, the more they are beaten the better they be," has reference to the manner of harvesting the ripe fruit. Evelyn says : "In Italy they arm the tops of long poles with nails and iron for the purpose [of loosening the fruit], and believe the beating improves the tree ; which I no more believe than I do that discipline would reform a shrew." He expresses no opinion on the question of beating dogs.

Sweet Chestnut (*Castanea sativa*).

Until about the middle of the last century the Chestnut was generally regarded as a genuine native of these islands. It is true that botanists felt that so large and longevous a tree, if native, should be found in the natural forests of this country, or even forming pure forest. These things they did not find, but, on the other hand, they were shown beams in ancient buildings, including Westminster Abbey, which were believed to be Chestnut-wood, and this evidence seemed to point to the fact that Chestnut timber was grown much more plentifully in this country at the period when these old buildings were erected. Dr. Lindley, however, set the matter at rest by examination of the reputed Chestnut beams in the roof of Westminster Abbey, and proved that they were of Durmast Oak. A similar examination of the timbers of the old Louvre in Paris, which were also reputed to be Chestnut, gave a similar result. A comparison of sections across the grain of Oak and Chestnut allows of no possibility of mistake, and it is now known that whilst the wood of young Chestnuts is tough and durable, that from old trees is brittle and comparatively worthless, except for firewood, which is exactly the opposite of Oak-wood. It is now generally agreed that its real home is in Asia Minor and Greece, whence it was

S

introduced to Italy in very remote times, and has since spread over most of temperate Europe, its seeds ripening and sowing themselves wherever the vine flourishes. We appear to be indebted to our friends the Romans for its introduction to Britain, who no doubt hoped to utilize the fruit for food, as at home—a hope that must have been disappointed, for its crops, even in the South of England, are very fitful, and the nuts quite small.

In suitable situations the Chestnut is of larger proportions and greater length of life even than the Oak. In the South of England it will attain a height of from sixty to eighty feet in fifty or sixty years, and if growing in deep porous loam, free from carbonate of lime, and sheltered from strong winds and frosts, it builds up an erect massive column. Hamerton has said of such a tree: " His expression is that of sturdy strength ; his trunk and limbs are built, not like those of Apollo, but like the trunk and limbs of Hercules." Under less suitable conditions the undivided trunk is little more than ten feet long ; then it divides off into several huge limbs, and so the general character of the tree is altered, and it presents much the appearance of having been pollarded. The branches have a horizontal and downward habit of growth, the extremities of the lowest ones often being but little above the earth. The fine elliptical leaves are nine or ten inches in length, of a rich green, that is enhanced by the polished surface, which " brings up" the colour. Their edges are cut into long pointed teeth. Towards autumn they pale to light yellow, and then deepen into gold on their way to the final brown of the fallen leaf, which, by the way, is a great enricher of the soil where the Chestnut is grown.

The flowers, though individually small and inconspicuous, are rather striking, from their association in cylindrical yellow catkins, about six inches long, which hang from the axils of the leaves. The free end of this catkin consists of male flowers, each with

Pl. 140.

S 136.

Sweet Chestnut—summer.

Pl. 141.

Bole of Sweet Chestnut.

a number of stamens enclosed in a perianth or calyx of five or six green leaves. The female flowers, nearer the base of the catkin, are two or three together, in a prickly four-lobed "cupule," or involucre, and consist each of a calyx closely investing a taper-ing ovary, whose summit bears from five to eight radiating

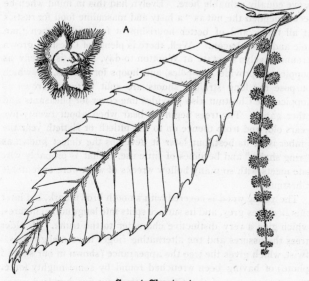

Sweet Chestnut.

A, fruit.

stigmas, the number corresponding with the cells into which the ovary is divided. Each cell contains two seed-eggs, but as a rule only one in each flower develops. As development of the ovary and seeds progresses, the cupule also grows, and ulti-mately entirely surrounds the cluster with the hedgehog-like coat in which the nuts are contained when ripe. Then it splits open and discloses the two or three glossy brown nuts. The Chestnut is in flower from May to July, and the nuts drop in October. They form an important article of food in South Europe, where they are produced in abundance, and there can be little doubt that the importers of the tree to this country believed it would prove equally valuable here. Evelyn had this in mind when he recommended the nut as "a lusty and masculine food for rustics at all times, and of better nourishment for husbandmen than cole and rusty bacon." Well, there is plenty of Chestnut grown around Evelyn's estate at Wootton to-day, but it is chiefly as coppice, to provide hop-poles, and hoops for barrels, for which purpose the long straight shoots are split in two. Grown as coppice, the Chestnut also provides fine cover for pheasants and other game. The trees begin to bear when about twenty-five years old, and from thence on to the fiftieth or sixtieth year the timber is at its best, but later it develops the defect known as "ring shake," and becomes of little use. That is probably why one meets with so many hollow wrecks of what were once noble Chestnuts.

The young wood is covered with smooth brown bark, but later this becomes grey, and its surface splits into longitudinal fissures, which give a very distinctive character to the trunk. In older trees the fissures and the alternating ridges have a slight spiral twist, which gives the tree the appearance (shown in our second photo) of having been wrenched round by some mighty force. The average age of the Chestnut is about five hundred years, but there have been in this country many old trees that were much older, if any reliance could be placed in local tradition. There was—we fear there is little of it still remaining—the great Tortworth Chestnut in Lord Ducies' park at Tortworth Court. In 1820 it was found to have a girth of fifty-two feet. Evelyn refers to it in his "Sylva," and tells us that in the reign of King Stephen it already bore the title of the Great Chestnut of Tortworth.

The name Chestnut appears to be a modification of the old Latin name *Castanea*, through the French form *Chataigner*. The Latin is said to be derived from Kastanum, a town in Thessaly, but it is more likely that the presence of Chestnut-trees gave a name to the town, as has happened so many times in our own country with various trees, the Chestnut included.

Horse Chestnut (*Æsculus hippocastanum*).

Our placing the Chestnut and the Horse Chestnut into juxtaposition must not be understood as a recognition of any relationship that may be implied in their names, but rather the reverse—to accentuate the differences that exist between them, and which have led botanists to separate them widely in all systems of classification. Although the fruits are suffi-ciently similar to have suggested the name Chestnut being applied to this, with a qualifying prefix, they have been produced by flowers of entirely different character. Evelyn tells us that the word Horse was added because of its virtues in "curing horses broken-winded and other cattle of coughs," a statement for which he was no doubt indebted to Parkinson (1640), who says, "Horse Chestnuts are given in the East Country, and so through all Turkie, unto Horses to cure them of the cough, shortnesse of winde, and such other dis-eases ;" but seeing that, in this country at least, horses refuse to touch them, there can be little doubt that the name was given to indicate their inferiority to the Sweet Chestnut, and by a process only too well known to the student of early botanical literature, the name was afterwards held to be proof of their medicinal value to horses.

The Horse Chestnut is a native of the mountain regions of Greece, Persia, and Northern India, and is believed to have been introduced to Britain about 1550. It is not a tree that will be found in the woodlands, or even by the wayside, except when it is behind a fence; yet it constantly greets the rambler who has left the suburban gardens behind him, and in the public parks—notably the magnificent avenue of Bushey Park—where by contrast it exhibits itself as the grandest of all flowering trees. Though the stout cylindrical bole is short, its erect trunk towers to a height of eighty or a hundred feet, supporting the massive pyramid, beautiful on account of its fine foliage and handsome flowers alike. The stout branches take an upward direction at first, then stretch outward and curve downwards, though in winter, when relieved of the weight of foliage, their extremities curl sharply upward, and the great buds in spring are almost erect.

These brown buds, with their numerous wraps and liberal coating of varnish, afford considerable interest to the suburban dweller in early spring. He watches their gradual swelling, and the polish that comes upon them through the daily melting of their varnish under the influence of sunshine. Then the outer scales fall flat, the upper parts show green and loose; there is a perceptible lengthening of the shoot, which leaves a space between those outer wraps and the folded leaves. Next the leaflets separate and assume a horizontal position as they expand. Then probably there comes a frost, and next morning the leaflets are all hanging down, almost blackened, flaccid and dejected-looking. A warm southerly rain, followed by sunshine, reinvigorates them, and we see that the lengthening of the shoot has actually brought the incipient flower-spike clear into view. By about the second week in May the pyramid is clothed with bold handsome foliage, against which the conical spikes of white blossoms, tinged with crimson and dotted with yellow, stand out conspicuously.

The leaves are almost circular, but broken up, finger-fashion, into seven toothed leaflets of different sizes, which appear to have started as ovals, but the necessity for not overcrowding

Flowers of Sweet Chestnut.

Pl. 142.

Pl. 143.

Sweet Chestnut—winter.

their neighbours has necessitated the portion nearest the leaf-stalk taking a wedge shape. The large size of these leaves —as much as eighteen inches across—leads the non-botanical to regard the leaflets as being full leaves. On emerging from

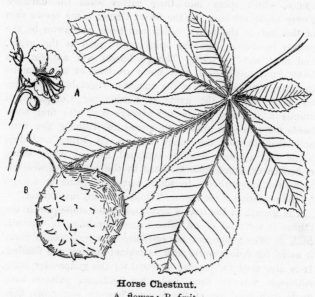

Horse Chestnut.
A, flower ; B, fruit.

the bud the leaves are seen to be covered with down, but as they expand this is thrown off.

The flowers consist of a bell-shaped calyx with five lobes, supporting five separate petals, pure white in colour, but splashed and dotted with crimson and yellow towards the base of the upper ones, to indicate the way to the honey-glands. There are seven curved stamens, and in their midst a longer curved style proceeding from a roundish ovary with three cells. In each cell there are two seed-eggs, but as a rule only one egg in two of the cells develops into a "nut." The ovary develops into a large fleshy bur, with short stout spines, which splits into three valves when the dark-red glossy seeds are ripe. In the Sweet Chestnut the brown skin of the nut is the ovary, which had been overgrown by the prickly involucre; here the spiny green shell is the ovary, and the "nut" a seed. Though horses will not eat this bitter fruit, cattle, deer, and sheep are fond of it. Pounded in water, it becomes one of the numerous vegetable substitutes for soap. Under the name of Konker, or Conqueror, it affords a seasonal joy to the average boy, who first bombards the tree with sticks and stones to dislodge the fruit, and then threads the ruddy konkers on string and does battle with a chum similarly equipped, the one whose string is broken or pulled from his hand by the conflict of weapons being the vanquished. In some parts the game is led off by the recitation of the rhyme, "Oblionker! my fust konker."

The growth of the tree is very rapid, and consequently the timber is soft and of no value where durability is required. Still, its even grain and susceptibility to a high polish make it useful for indoor work, such as cabinet-making and flooring. It is also used for making charcoal for the gunpowder mills. Although Salvator Rosa and other landscape painters have made such good use of the Sweet Chestnut pictorially, they have utterly neglected the Horse Chestnut; and Hamerton hints that the cause of this neglect is the artist's inability to represent its large flowers and leaves by the landscape painter's ordinary method of laying on masses of colour: this requires drawing. The tree begins to produce fruit about its twentieth year, and continues to do so nearly every year. Its age is estimated as about two hundred years. The bark, at first smooth, breaks into irregular scales and in old trees

Horse Chestnut — summer.

Pl. 144

Fruits of Horse Chestnut.

Pl. 145.

Pl. 146.

Bole of Horse Chestnut.

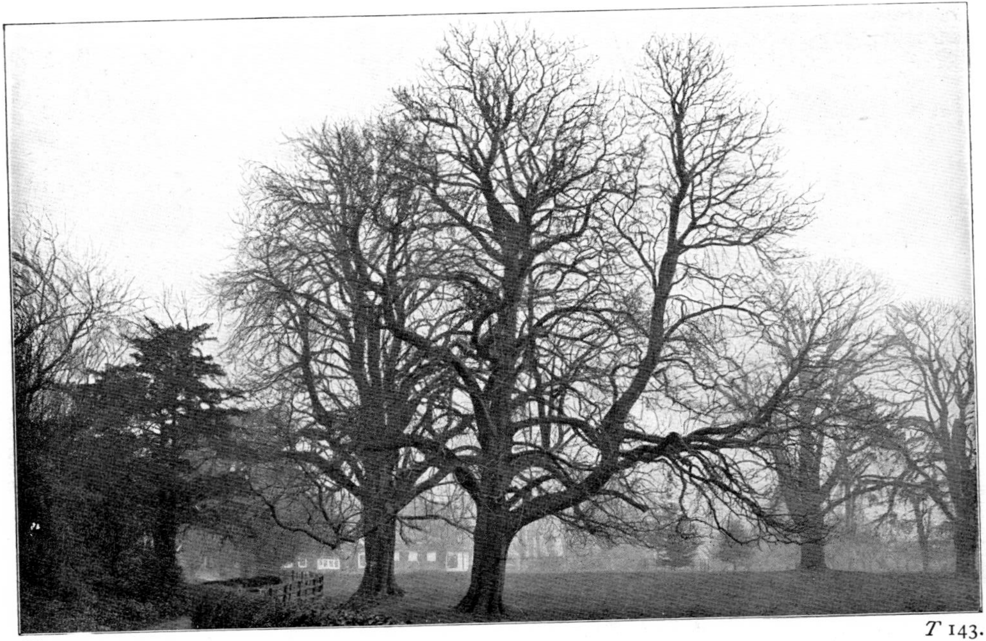

Horse Chestnut—winter.

Pl. 147

a twist may be developed, as illustrated by our photo of the bole.

The generic name *Æsculus* (from Latin *esca*, food) has no real connection with the tree, the ancients having given it to some species of Oak with edible acorns (*vide* Pliny), but by some unknown means it has become transferred to a tree whose fruit is far too bitter to be eaten by man.

The Red-flowered Horse Chestnut (*Æsculus carnea*) is a smaller and less vigorous tree. Its origin is unknown, but it is believed to be a garden hybrid that made its appearance about 1820.

The Bay Tree (*Laurus nobilis*).

The Bay is the true Laurel, of whose leaves and berries the wreaths were made in ancient days for poets and conquerors. Naturally it is more of a shrub than a tree, for though it often attains a height of sixty feet, it persists in sending up so many suckers that the tree-like character is lost. In cultivation, however, it is often grown on a single stem, as well as formed by cutting into arbours and arches. We call to mind a Cornish village, where a garden enclosure in its square (or "plestor," as Gilbert White would say) was surrounded by about a dozen Bays so grown. Bays grow abundantly in the gardens of South Cornwall, and we always connected their general cultivation with the pilchard fishery. Certainly, these trees in the plestor were very convenient in the autumn and winter, for the leaves are an essential ingredient in the proper composition of that seductive dish, marinated pilchards, to which they impart their peculiar aromatic flavour.

The Bay is a native of Southern Europe, whence it was introduced at some date prior to 1562. Prior says the name is the old Roman *bacca* (a berry), altered "by the usual omission of 'c' between the two vowels," this plant having become the

T

bacca par excellence, because its berries were articles of commerce.

The evergreen leaves are lance-shaped, without teeth, and arranged alternately on the branchlets. Not all the trees produce the berries, for the sexes are in distinct individuals,

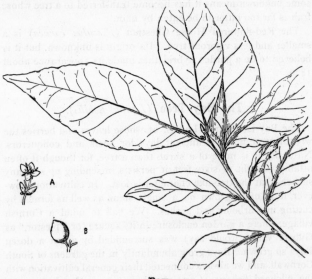

Bay.
A, flower ; B, fruit.

and all the white or yellowish four-parted flowers on one tree are stamen-bearing, whilst on another individual they all bear ovaries and no stamens. The berries, at first green, ultimately become of a dark purple hue. The flowers will be found in April or May ; the ripe berries in October. The Bay is grown chiefly as a shrubbery ornament, and can only survive our winters out-of-doors in the South of England.

Pl. 148.

Bay.

Pl. 149.

Laburnum.

Laburnum (*Laburnum vulgare*).

Although the Laburnums of our parks and gardens have all come from seed, and themselves produce an abundance of it, we do not meet with wayside " escapes" as we might expect to do, having regard to the habit of the tree and the fact that it is comparatively indifferent respecting character of soil. Possibly a remark of Loudon's may explain this. He says that rabbits are exceedingly fond of the bark, and it may be that they destroy any young trees that are unprotected by palings or netting. The tree produces such a glorification of many an ordinary suburban road, when its flowering time comes round, that one would like to note its effect as a common object of the hillside and the woodland, against a background furnished by our more sober native trees.

The Laburnum is at home in the mountain forests of Central and Southern Europe, but there is no record of its introduction to Britain. We do know, however, that it has been with us for more than three centuries, for Gerarde, in his " Herbal," published 1597, refers to it as growing in his garden. It belongs to the great Pea and Bean family (*Leguminosæ*), and is very closely related to the Common Broom, whose solitary flowers those of the Laburnum's drooping racemes nearly resemble. Ordinarily it is only a low tree of about twenty feet in height, but in favourable situations it may attain to thirty feet or more. Some of the larger Laburnums, however, are of a distinct species (*L. alpinus*).

The pale round branches are clothed with leaves that are divided into three oval-lance-shaped leaflets, covered on the underside with silvery down. Both leaves and golden flowers appear simultaneously in May, but from the fact that the latter are gathered into numerous long pendulous racemes, their blaze of colour makes the leaves almost invisible. Tennyson's description of its flowering—" Laburnum, dropping wells of fire"—

is fine, but we rather prefer Cowper's "rich in streaming gold," as embodying a more exact colour idea. The flowers are succeeded by long downy legumes or pods, like those of the bean and pea, containing many seeds, which are of a dangerously violent emetic character when introduced to the human stomach.

Laburnum.
A, seed-pod.

The dark wood is of coarse grain ; but, in spite of this, hard and enduring, and taking a good polish. It is chiefly used by musical instrument makers, turners, and cabinet-makers.

Laburnum is the old Latin name, which is thus rather fanci-fully explained by Prior, " an adjective from L. *labor*, denoting what belongs to the *hour* of *labour,* and which may allude to its closing its leaflets together at night, and expanding them by day." Common local names are Golden Chain, suggested by the strings of flowers, and Bean-trefoil and Pea-tree, having reference to the leaves and legumes respectively.

The Locust Tree (*Robinia pseudacacia*).

Although the Locust, or False Acacia, is little planted now, it is only paying the penalty for having had its merits enormously exaggerated ; just as human reputations sometimes sink into oblivion after a season of popularity achieved by the persistent "booming" of influential friends. The friend in this case was William Cobbett, who, on his return from the United States, about 1820, preached salvation to the timber grower through the planting of Robinia : "nothing in the timber way could be so great a benefit as the general cultivation of this tree." So great was the demand thus created that Cobbett himself started a nursery for the propagation and supply of Robinias, and so great is the virtue of a name that people refused the Locust-trees that every nurseryman had in stock and wished to sell, and would be content with nothing but Cobbett's Robinias, which could not be produced fast enough for the demand! They thought it was an entirely new introduction, though it had been grown in this country as an ornamental tree for nearly two centuries ! Its wood is hard, strong, and durable, but liable to crack, and of limited utility.

The Locust was introduced to Europe from North America early in the seventeenth century, and was then thought to be identical with the African Acacia. Linnæus named the genus in honour of Jean Robin, a French botanist, whose son, an official at the Jardin des Plantes, was the first to cultivate the tree in Europe.

It is a tree of light and graceful proportions, its branches

being long and slender, and the long narrow leaves being broken
up into a large number of small oval leaflets, arranged *pinnately*,
that is, featherwise.   The stipules, which are found at the base
of the leaf-stalk in many plants, are in this genus converted into
sharp spines.   The flowers, of similar pea-shape to those of the

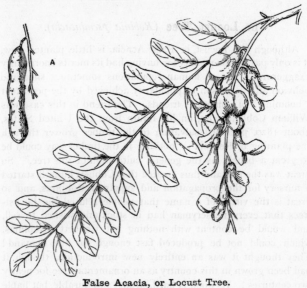

False Acacia, or Locust Tree.

A, seed-pod.

Laburnum, are white and fragrant.   They are in long loose
racemes, which droop from the axils of the leaves in May.   The
legumes are very thin, and of a dark-brown hue.

This was one of the first American trees introduced to
Europe, and its name of Locust came with it, the missionaries
believing it must be the tree upon whose fruit, with the addition

Pl. **1**50.

Locust Tree—summer.

Pl. 151

Bole of Locust Tree.

of wild honey, John the Baptist supported himself in the wilderness. It is also known as Silver Chain, in contradistinction to the Gold Chain or Laburnum ; also as White Laburnum.

The Larch (*Larix europæa*).

An enormous number of exotic Coniferous trees are at the present time commonly grown in our parks and pleasure grounds, and even our woods show a considerable variety beyond the Scots Pine and Yew that Nature has alone given us as timber trees in this order. To attempt to give even a very brief account of all these in a pocket volume, in addition to almost the entire woody Flora indigenous to these islands, would be manifestly absurd. We can, however, deal with a few representative species of these exotics, and we give the Larch the first place by reason of its present plentifulness in extensive unmixed woods and plantations.

The Larch is naturally a tree of the mountains, and ascends to a greater elevation even than the Spruce Fir. Unmixed forests of Larch in the Bavarian Alps occur between 3000 and 6000 feet above sea-level, and on the central Swiss Alps it ascends to nearly 7000 feet. A long winter of real cold is necessary for its full development and the ripening of its wood, and for that reason the timber of Larch grown in England is inferior to that grown in its native countries, because our winters are either short or mild, and neither gives the tree the full rest it needs. It is a European tree, and was introduced— though not in any numbers—to England at some date prior to 1629. For 150 years it appears to have been cultivated here merely as an ornamental garden tree. Then attention was called to its value as a timber tree, and the Society of Arts offered gold medals for Larch planting and essays upon its economic importance. Already (1728) the second Duke of Atholl had begun those experiments in Larch growing for

timber which have been continued by his successors on a vast
scale, the fourth Duke planting 27,000,000 Larch-trees on

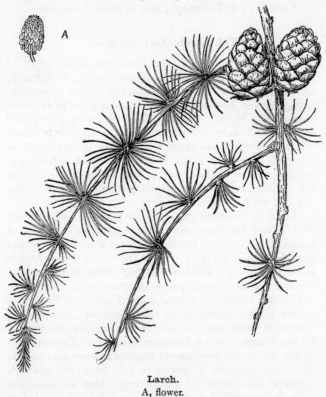

A

Larch.
A, flower.

15,000 acres of barren land.   Their example has been copied on
a smaller scale all over the country.

The Larch is a lofty tree, with a very straight tapering trunk

Locust—winter.

used for tanning, and Venice turpentine is a product of the tree. Unlike most Conifers, it has the power of sending out new shoots when the branches have been removed close up to the stem.

Larch plantations sometimes present the appearance of death whilst they are still covered with foliage, but the leaves are yellow and twisted. This most frequently occurs in the case of trees between the ages of ten and fourteen years, and is due to the depredations of a leaf-mining caterpillar, which ultimately changes into a minute moth, the Larch-miner (*Coleophora laricella*). It feeds in the interior of the Larch-needles, and therefore is beyond the reach of destruction, except by felling and burning affected trees, to prevent the spread of the pest. Its ravages keep the tree in ill-health, and apparently prepare the way for the deadly attack of another small enemy, known as the Larch Canker—the fungus *Dasyscypha calycina*. Sickly trees are also liable to the attentions of a Wood-wasp (*Sirex noctilio*), whose appearance is usually the cause of a little terror in nervous persons. It has two pairs of smoky transparent wings, and its stout, straight, blue body terminates in a long slender point. Its large white grub spends two or three years tunnelling towards the heart of the tree and out to the bark again, but rarely attacks sound trees. It sometimes makes its appearance in a house from wood that has been used for building purposes.

The Silver Fir (*Abies pectinata*).

Evelyn has left on record the fact that a two-year-old specimen of the Silver Fir was planted in Harefield Park, near Uxbridge, in the year 1603, and this is usually regarded as the date of its introduction to England, though the evidence is by no means conclusive. Its home is in the mountain regions of Central and Southern Europe. Its highest range

Pl. 156.

Flowers and Cone of Larch.

Pl. 157.

Silver Fir.

appears to be on the Pyrenees, where it is found at an elevation
of 6500 feet, forming pure forests of considerable area.
Specimens have been recorded in Southern Germany that have
attained a height of nearly 200 feet, but in this country a more
usual stature is from 100 to 120 feet, with a bole girth between
10 and 15 feet. Its trunk is straight and erect, tapering gently,
and covered with smooth bark, of a greyish-brown colour,

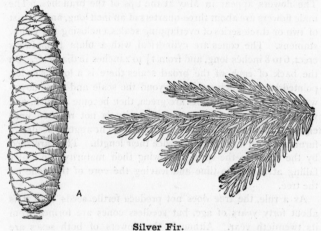

Silver Fir.

A, cone.

which in aged specimens becomes rugged and fissured longi-
tudinally, as shown in our photo, and of a silvery grey colour.
It retains its lower branches for a period of forty to fifty years,
but after that age they begin to fall off. Whilst the tree is
growing up—which is, roughly speaking, during its first two
hundred years—the crown forms a slender bush; but its vertical
growth completed, the crown grows laterally, and becomes flat-
topped. Its life-period covers about four hundred years.

The leaves are flat and slender, not in bundles, as in the Scots Pine, but arranged along the branchlets in two or three dense ranks. They are dark, rich green above, about an inch long, and on the flattened underside there is a bluish-white stripe on each side of the midrib, which gives a silvery appearance to the foliage when upturned, as is usual on the fertile branches. These leaves endure from six to nine years. The flowers appear in May at the tips of the branches. The male flowers are about three-quarters of an inch long, and consist of two or three series of overlapping scales, enclosing the yellow stamens. The cones are cylindrical, with a blunt top, always erect, 6 to 8 inches long, and from $1\frac{1}{4}$ to 2 inches in diameter. On the back of each of the broad scales there is a long, slender, pointed bract, which extends beyond the scale and turns downward. At first these cones are green, then become reddish, and when mature are brown; but maturity is not reached until eighteen months after their appearance. The angular seeds are furnished with a broad wing twice their length. They are shed by the cones in the spring following their maturity, the scales falling at the same time and leaving the core of the cone on the tree.

As a rule, the tree does not produce fertile seeds until it is about forty years of age, but seedless cones are formed from its twentieth year. Although the flowers of both sexes are found on the same tree, it may be that for a series of years only cones are produced. Until the Silver Fir is about twelve years old its growth is slow, and its annual increase is only a few inches, but later it will be as many feet. During this early stage spring frosts often destroy the leader-shoot, but its place is taken by another shoot, and soon the symmetry of the tree is restored. If this occurs at a later stage, however, the tree bears evidence of it in a forked trunk. It is a deep-rooting species, with a branching tap-root, and succeeds best in an open soil that is moist without being wet.

Pl. 158.

Bole of Silver Fir.

Pl. 159.

Spruce Firs.

Pl. 160.

Bole of Spruce Fir.

Pl. 161.

Douglas Fir.

The timber, which has an irregular grain, is strong, and does not warp; but it is soft, and not enduring where it is exposed to the weather. It is yellowish-white in colour, and is largely used for all interior work.

The Spruce Fir (*Picea excelsa*).

Although we are compelled to class the Spruce among introduced species, it can lay claim to have been one of the older forest trees of Britain, for the upper beds of the Tertiary formations contain abundant evidence that the Spruce was a native here when those strata were laid down. Of its modern introduction there is no record, but from mention of it by Turner in his "Names of Herbes in Greke, Latin, Englishe, etc.," we know that it was at some date anterior to the publication of that work (1548). It is widely distributed as a native tree throughout the continent of Europe, with the exception of Denmark and Holland. It is the principal forest tree on the elevated tracts of Germany and Switzerland, and on the central Alpine ranges it reaches an altitude of 6500 feet. It is an extremely variable tree, but we cannot here deal with the varieties beyond saying that two principal forms, different in habit and in timber, are outwardly distinguished by one having red, the other green, cones.

The Spruce Fir is a tall and graceful tree with tapering trunk, 120 to 150 feet in height, though in this country its more usual stature, when full-grown, would be about 80 feet high, with a bole circumference of about 9 feet. At first covered with thin, smooth, warm-brown bark, in later life this breaks up into irregular scales, thin layers of which are cast off. Instead of a bushy crown, such as we see in the Silver Fir, the Spruce ends in a delicate spire, so familiar in the Christmas-tree, which is a Spruce Fir in the nursery stage. The branches are in very regular tiers from base to summit, and the branchlets go off almost opposite each other, densely clothed with the short grass-green needles. These are from a half to three-quarters of an inch in length, four-sided, and ending in a fine sharp point. They endure for six or seven years.

The flowers are produced near the ends of last year's shoots,

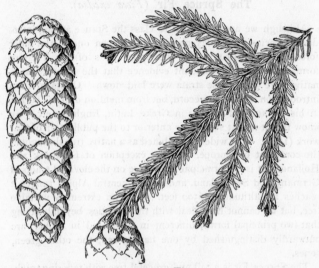

Spruce Fir.

those with stamens being borne singly or in clusters of two or three. They are about three-quarters of an inch in length, and of a yellow colour, tinged with pink. The cones, which hang downwards, are almost cylindrical, about 5 inches long and $1\frac{1}{2}$ inches in diameter. The pale brown scales are thin, and loosely overlap. The seeds, of which there are two under each scale, are very small, with a transparent brown wing, five times the

Pl. 162.   *U* 156.

Bole of Douglas Fir.

Cone of Spruce Fir.

Pl. 163.

length of the seed. The flowers appear in May, and the seeds are not ripe until nearly a year later.

The tree is a shallow rooter, the roots going off horizontally in all directions a little below the surface, and becoming intimately matted with those of neighbouring trees. This surface-rooting often leads to disaster in plantations and forests of Spruce, for it is least able of all the firs to withstand a gale, which will sometimes make a broad avenue through the plantation by toppling the trees one against another.

The wood of the Spruce Fir, though light, is even grained, elastic, and durable, and the straightness of its stem makes it very valuable for all purposes where great length and straightness are required, as for the masts of small vessels, ladders, scaffolding, telegraph-poles ; as well as for the varied uses the builder finds for its planks. It supplies resin and pitch, and most of the cheaper periodicals now issued largely owe their existence to the Spruce, for its fibres reduced to pulp are made into the paper upon which they are printed. Although its growth during the first few years is rather slow, progress during the next twenty-five years is tolerably rapid, being at the rate of two or three feet per year, if in a favourable situation, and on moist light soil. When grown in a wood the Spruce loses its lower branches early, but when given sufficient "elbow-room," these remain to a good old age, so that from spire to earth the graceful cone of bright green is continuous.

The name Spruce is from the German *sprossen* (a sprout), in allusion to the numerous short branchlets that are a characteristic of the tree.

The Douglas Fir (*Pseudotsuga douglasii*).

Although the name of this tree in English and Latin might reasonably lead one to suppose that David Douglas, the intrepid botanical explorer, was the discoverer of it, that is not really so.

It was Archibald Menzies who first made it known to science, by means of herbarium specimens collected in 1792, when, as the companion of Vancouver, he visited the western coasts of North America. But Douglas, in his capacity of collector to the Royal Horticultural Society, landed at Fort Vancouver on the Columbia River in 1825, and not only sent home herbarium specimens, but seeds also, of this and several previously unknown Conifers. It was by means of these seeds that the Douglas Fir was introduced to Britain. It was already known by Lambert's name of *Abies taxifolia*, but Dr. Lindley, a short time previous to Douglas' untimely death, selected the tree as a suitable and enduring memorial of the enormous services Douglas had rendered, and named it *Abies douglasii*. Since then Carrière has split up the old genus *Abies* and placed *douglasii* in the new genus *Pseudotsuga*.

Under the most favourable natural conditions, as around Puget Sound and on the western slopes of the Sierra Nevada, the Douglas Fir grows to a height of 300 feet, with a girth of 30 to 40 feet, but on the drier slopes of the Rocky Mountains it is not more than 100 feet high. In Colorado, forests of Douglas Fir are found at an elevation of 11,000 feet. The tree has not been sufficiently long established in this country to say what dimensions it will reach, though it appears to have taken kindly to Ireland and to Devon and Cornwall, where the rate of growth of young trees is about 30 inches per annum. There are plenty of trees in these islands, planted about the year 1834, which have reached or passed 100 feet, and there is no doubt that towards our western coasts this height will be greatly exceeded. Some of these trees have long since produced cones, and from their seeds many young trees have been raised.

The Douglas Fir is of pyramidal outline, with the lowest branches bending to the ground under their weight of branchlets and leaves ; above, they spread horizontally, but the uppermost are more or less ascending. The branchlets are given off mostly

Stone Pine.

Pl. 164.

a three-clawed bract, whereof the middle claw or awn is very long. Several well-marked varieties of the Douglas Fir are also to be met with occasionally in parks and gardens.

The Douglas Fir produces excellent timber, and is a most valuable forest tree, not only on that account, but because of its adaptability to varying conditions of soil and climate. It is the most widely distributed of all American forest trees, and the area of its distribution is spread over thirty-two degrees of latitude, and from end to end of this range it has, in the words of Sargent, "to endure the fierce gales and long winters of the north, and the nearly perpetual sunshine of the Mexican Cordilleras ; to thrive in the rain and fog which sweep almost continuously along the Pacific coast range, and on the arid mountain slopes of the interior, where for months every year rain never falls." It appears to thrive best where the air is humid and the soil well drained. It begins to bear cones about its twenty-fifth year. The straight tapering trunk is largely used for the masts and spars of ships, its suitability for this purpose being evident to all visitors to Kew who have gazed at the flag-staff set up in the arboretum. This pole is 159 feet long, with a circumference of 6 feet at the base, tapering to 2 feet 2 inches at the top, and weighing about 3 tons. It was brought from Vancouver Island, and an examination of its rings before it was set up showed that it represented the growth of about 250 years. The full life of the Douglas Fir is estimated to be about 750 years.

The Stone Pine (*Pinus pinea*).

Between the tall, graceful spire of the Douglas Fir and the squat, heavy, umbrella-like head of the Stone Pine, there is an enormous contrast. It must be confessed that the Stone Pine is less beautiful than picturesque, a point that strongly commends is to the landscape painter working in the countries bordering

Pl. 166.

Austrian Pine.

Pl. 167.

Bole of Austrian Pine.

the Mediterranean, in which region it is native. The date of
its introduction to Britain is not known, but it has been in cultivation here certainly for more than three centuries and a half,
for Turner mentions it in his " Names of Herbes in Greke, Latin,
Englishe, Duch, and Frenche," published in 1548. In its native

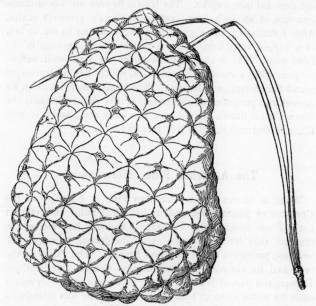

Stone Pine, cone and leaves.

countries it attains a height of sixty to eighty feet, but in this
country the finest examples are only about thirty-five feet,
whilst ordinary British-grown examples are only half that
height. Its trunk, covered with rugged, and deeply fissured,
thick, red-grey bark, forks at no great distance from the roots,

and sends off massive spreading branches of great length. For several years the young tree produces short single leaves, but later leaves are five or six inches long, slender, and of a bright green tint, in pairs, united at their base by a pale sheath. These leaves endure for two or three years. The pollen-bearing flowers are crowded into a spike. The female flowers are about three-quarters of an inch long, composed of pale greenish scales. After fertilization, these grow to a length of four to six inches, of a rugged oval form and red-brown colour, ripening in the third year. The scales of these cones are somewhat wedge-shaped, with a stout rhomboid boss, which has a depression round the central protuberance. The seeds, which are eaten for dessert and preserved as sweetmeats in the countries where the Stone Pine is native, are enclosed in a bony shell, and it is from this circumstance that the tree gets its name.

The Austrian Pine (*Pinus laricio*).

What is known as the Austrian Pine is a variety of the Corsican or Larch Pine, and its botanical name correctly set out is *Pinus laricio*, var. *austriaca*. The name has reference to the fact that its chief home as an indigenous tree is in the southern provinces of the Austrian Empire. The range of the type and its varieties together includes Central and Southern Europe, and part of Western Asia. It is a comparatively recent addition to our sylva in both forms, for the type was introduced in 1759, in the belief that it was a maritime form of the Scots Pine, but the variety *austriaca* was first sent out by Lawson and Son, the Edinburgh nurserymen, in 1835.

The typical species (Corsican Pine) is a slender tree of somewhat pyramidal form, growing to the height of 80 to 120 feet. The Austrian Pine, though a large tree, is of smaller proportions—from 60 to 80 feet high—but with stouter and

Pl. 168.

Cones of Austrian Pine.

Pl. 169.

X 163.

Cedar of Lebanon.

longer branches, and denser foliage. The leaves, which vary from three to five inches in length, are sheathed in pairs, convex on the outer side, rigid, glossy, dark green, and with toothed

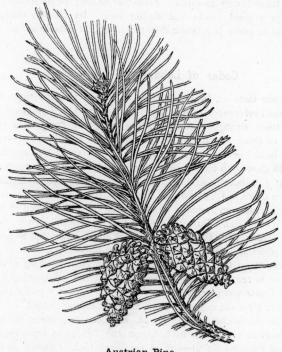

Austrian Pine.

margins. The cone is conical (!), with a rounded base, two to three inches in length, and its position on the branch is almost horizontal, the scales somewhat similar to those of the Scots Pine, but with stronger bosses, and of a yellowish-brown colour.

polished. It takes about seventeen months to become full grown and ripen the seeds.

The Austrian Pine is one of those that do well on poor soils, and takes kindly to chalk. From the density of its foliage, it makes a good shade and shelter tree. Its timber, though coarse in grain, is very durable, and useful for outside work.

Cedar of Lebanon (*Cedrus libani*).

Made familiar, by name at least, from very early times by frequent references to it in the books of the Old Testament, it is rather strange that so hardy a tree was not one of the first of those introduced for ornament into Britain. It is true that local legends attaching to some old Cedars in this country credit them with having been planted in " the spacious times of great Elizabeth "—as the great Cedar at Whitton, Middlesex, blown down in 1779; but, on the other hand, we have the fact that no mention is made of the Cedar by John Evelyn in his " Sylva " (1664). This, it is true, is only negative evidence ; but it is strong none the less, for it is not at all likely that so keen and pious an arboriculturist would have omitted mention of so noteworthy a tree had such been growing here when he wrote. There is reason to believe, however, that the still-existing Enfield Cedar was planted about the date of Evelyn's publication by Dr. Uvedale, master of the Enfield Grammar School.

The researches of Sir J. D. Hooker, subsequent to his memorable expedition to Lebanon and Taurus in 1860, established the specific identity of the three Cedars known as the Mount Atlas Cedar, the Cedar of Lebanon, and the Deodar. Though the arboriculturist still treats them as distinct species, they are scientifically regarded as geographical forms of one species. For convenience we here adopt the arboriculturist's view.

Pl. 170.

Bole of Cedar of Lebanon.

Pl. 171.

Deodar.

The Cedar varies greatly—no tree more so—in height and general outline, according to situation and environment, and though the stature of well-grown trees in this country may be correctly stated as from 50 to 80 feet, we are not without examples of 100 and 120 feet where the conditions have been specially favourable. There is one of 120 feet at Strathfieldsaye, and among the numerous fine Cedars at Goodwood there is the celebrated Great Cedar, 90 feet high, with a bole 25 feet in

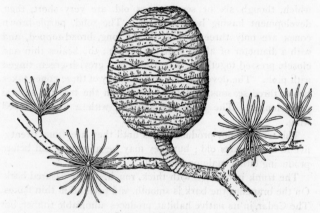

Cedar of Lebanon.

circumference, and a broad conical head whose base has a diameter of 130 feet. But the Cedar, as usually seen on lawns and in parks, has a low, rounded, or flattened top, the great spreading arms having grown more rapidly than the trunk. Thus grown, the huge bole has seldom any great length, throwing out these timber branches at from six to ten feet from the ground, and immediately afterwards the trunk is divided into several stems. From these the main branches take a curving direction, at first ascending, but the part furthest from the trunk becoming almost horizontal. It is chiefly at the extremity of the branches that the branchlets and leaves are produced.

The evergreen leaves last for three, four, or five years, and are of needle-shape, varying in length from a little less to a little more than an inch. They are produced in a similar manner to those of the Larch—in tufts that are arranged spirally round dwarf shoots, mostly on the upper side of the branchlets. The male flowers are to be found at the extremity of branchlets which, though six or seven years old, are very short, their development having been arrested. The solid, purple-brown cones are only three or four inches long, broad-topped, and with a diameter of about half the length ; the scales thin and closely pressed together ; they are at first greyish-green, tinged with pink. The development and maturity of these cones takes two or three seasons, and they remain on the tree for several years longer. The seeds are angular, with a wedge-shaped wing.

The trees do not produce cones until they are from twenty-five to thirty years old ; but they may be a century old before producing either male or female flowers.

The trunk is covered with thick, rough, deeply fissured bark. On the branches the bark is smooth. and peels off in thin flakes. The Cedar, in its native habitat, produces admirable timber, but that of trees grown in our own country is described by Loudon as "reddish-white, light and spongy, easily worked, but very apt to shrink and warp, and by no means durable." For these reasons the tree is grown almost solely for ornament.

The name Cedar is supposed to be derived from the Arabic *kedroum*, or *kèdre* (power), and has reference to its majestic proportions and strong timber.

The Deodar, or Indian Cedar (*Cedrus deodara*).

Although, as we have indicated, the differences between the Cedar of Lebanon and the Cedar of Himalaya are not such as can be scientifically accepted as constituting specific distinctness, they are sufficient to at once strike the ordinary observer. In proportion to the height of the trunk, for example, the main branches are much shorter, the result being a more regular pyramidal outline, terminating in a light spire. The terminal shoots of the branches are longer, more slender, and quite pendulous. These differences, though really slight, transform the rather heavy majesty of the Cedar, as represented by *C. libani*, into one of graceful beauty. Although the experience of sixty years has sadly falsified the high hopes entertained as to the suitability of the Deodar for cultivation in this country as a timber tree, its value for ornamental purposes and in landscape gardening has not been impaired.

The headquarters of the Deodar are in the mountains of north-west India, where it forms forests at various altitudes above 3500 feet. Its vertical distribution, indeed, extends to a height of 12,000 feet, but its principal habitat lies between 6000 and 10,000 feet. Deodar timber produced in its native forests is exceedingly durable, being compact and even grained, not liable to warp or split, and standing the test of being alternately wet and dry. Loudon states that when a building, which had been erected by the Emperor Akbar in the latter part of the sixteenth century, was pulled down between 1820 and 1825, the Deodar timber used in its construction was found to be so sound that it was again used in building a house for Rajah Shah. And Brandis tells of very much more ancient bridges in Srunagar, whose piers are of Deodar wood, and appear to be as yet unaffected by decay.

It is to the Hon. W. L. Melville that we are indebted for the introduction of the Deodar to Britain in 1831, and during the

Y

next ten years many young trees were raised here from seeds.
Favourably impressed by the rapidity of growth of these seedlings, the government, fearing a coming shortage of Oak for naval
purposes, imported and distributed large numbers of Deodar
seeds, and high estimates were formed of the future value of

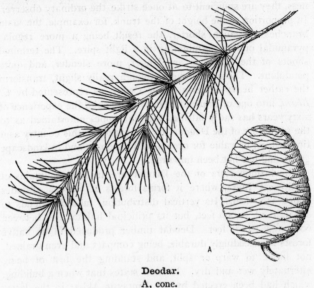

Deodar.
A, cone.

these trees. But in framing these estimates one important
factor was omitted—the uncertainty of the British climate, with
its rapid changes, "everything by turns, and nothing long." A
score or two of years served to demonstrate that such conditions
were opposed to the longevity and uniform development that
produced sound timber on the Indian mountains; and to-day
the Deodar is not mentioned among the trees that are to bring

Pl. 172.

Bole of Deodar.

Pl. 173.

Y 169.

Lawson's Cypress.

riches to the British timber grower. In spite of this failure, there are to be seen in many parts of these islands fine young Deodars of forty or fifty years, and from fifty to seventy feet in height.

There is no necessity for repeating the particulars already given respecting the Cedar of Lebanon, and which apply to the Deodar with such modifications as are indicated in the first paragraph above. Specimens grown where they have sufficient space for spreading out their long arms, retain their branches to the base of the trunk, and if these are cut off they can reproduce them. Several nursery varieties—with golden (*aurea*), silvery (*argentea*), or more intense green (*viridis*) foliage than the type —have appeared as a result of European cultivation.

Lawson's Cypress (*Cupressus lawsoniana*).

Lawson's Cypress belongs to that section of Conifers which includes the Junipers and Thuias, and is a representative of the North American Sylva. It is a native of South Oregon and North California, where it is believed to have been first discovered by Jeffrey, about 1852. Two years later seeds were received by Messrs. Lawson, the Edinburgh nurserymen, from Mr. William Murray, and from these seeds were raised the first young trees of this species sent out by the firm. The name was bestowed in honour of Mr. Charles Lawson, the then head of the firm, and by this name it is generally known in Europe, but in the United States it is the Port Orford Cypress. At Port Orford, on the Oregon coast, according to Sargent, "it forms one of the most prolific and beautiful coniferous forests of the continent, unsurpassed in the variety and luxuriance of its undergrowth of Rhododendrons, Vacciniums, Raspberries, Buckthorns, and Ferns," and any one who has seen well-grown specimens in the pleasure-grounds of this country can easily realize something of the beauty of such a forest, though allowance has to be made for the fact that in forest growth the lower branches are lost at an early age.

In its native home the Lawson Cypress attains a height of between 120 and 150 feet, occasionally reaching 200 feet, with a base circumference of 40 feet. The thick brown bark splits into rounded scaly ridges. The short horizontal

Lawson Cypress.

branches divide a good deal towards their leafy extremities, which are curved, and commonly drooping. The leaves are little evergreen scales, which overlap, and being closely pressed to the branchlet, completely clothe and hide it. They are bright dark-green in colour, and endure for three or four years. The male flowers are produced at the tips of short branchlets, formed a year earlier. They are of cylindric form, crimson in colour, and each stamen bears from two to six anther-cells. The small "cones" are more or less globular, but instead of a large number of spirally arranged overlapping scales, as in the Pines and Firs, here there are only eight, whose edges at first join to form a box. When the "cone" is ripe these scales separate, to allow the escape of the seeds.

The Lawson Cypress produces a valuable wood, close-grained and strong, yet light. It is considered one of the most important timber trees of North America ; but in this country it has been planted solely with a view to its ornamental qualities. Its perfect hardiness and its freedom of growth may, with longer experience than half a century affords, lead to its being regarded as a timber producer here also.

The Common Cypress (*Cupressus sempervirens*) of the Mediterranean region and the East, of which poets have sung in all ages, has been cultivated in this country for at least three hundred and fifty years.

The Chili Pine (*Araucaria imbricata*).

The Chili Pine, or "Monkey Puzzle," is a familiar sight on suburban lawns, where, however, it seldom attains a large size or long retains health. The lower branches drop off, and the upper ones become brown, as though scorched. But away from ᵗhe smoke-laden atmosphere and uncongenial soils, some handsome and massive Araucarias may be seen rising from fair lawns, with dense branches curving at their tips, and regularly disposed in whorls from the dome-like head of the tree to the grass at its base. Such was the magnificent specimen at Dropmore that died in 1902, such is the fine tree at Woodstock, Co. Kilkenny, which now presumably takes the position of eminence in these islands hitherto held by the Dropmore example.

The Chili Pine is a native of Southern Chili, where it was discovered by a Spaniard, Don F. Dendariarena, in 1780, as he was prospecting for timber. About the same time two other Spaniards, Drs. Ruiz and Pavon, were botanizing in Chili, and came across the Araucaria, of which they sent herbarium speci-

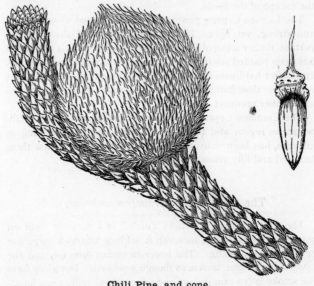

Chili Pine, and cone.
A, seed, with attached wing.

mens to Europe. But in spite of this three-fold opportunity for Spain, the actual introduction of the Araucaria to Europe must be credited to Britain. Archibald Menzies, who accompanied Captain Vancouver as botanist on his celebrated voyage, came across the tree in Chili, and brought home both seeds and

Pl. 174.

Bole of Lawson's Cypress.

Pl. 175.

Chili Pine.

young plants. One of these became a fine tree at Kew, where it was for many years the object of admiration and interest, but it perished in 1892.

The Araucaria forms extensive pine forests in the province of Arauco, from which it gets its name, and to whose inhabitants the seeds are a most important item of their food-supply. Not only do the trees in these forests lose their lower branches, but even those growing in the open plains of their native country have similarly bare trunks for nearly half their height. It is therefore a satisfaction to know that the finest specimens grown in this country have really surpassed those grown in their natural home. The height reached by old trees is from eighty to a hundred feet, with a trunk-girth of from sixteen to twenty-three feet. The tapering of this trunk is very slight, and a few of the stiff, spine-tipped leaves, with which its younger extremity is densely clothed, still remain attached in a dried-up condition far down the column. These leaves will have been observed to entirely cover the branches, not being restricted, as in most trees, to the newly formed branchlets and twigs. They are very hard, and endure for about fifteen years ; are about an inch and a quarter long, and overlap, though their sharp-pointed ends turn away from the branch.

The cylindrical male flowers are four or five inches long, borne singly or in small clusters. It was formerly supposed that the sexes were on separate trees, but though many individuals only produce flowers of one kind, this is by no means the general rule. The female flowers are about four inches long, almost round in shape, but broader at the base than above. They are covered with long, narrow, overlapping scales, beneath which are found the seeds when the flower has developed into the brown cone, which is six inches in diameter. The scales are then easily detached ; in fact, when the seeds are ripe, the cone falls to pieces. The seed is about an inch and a half long, enclosed in a hard, thin shell.

The Chili Pine does not succeed in this country unless it is given pure air, sunshine, abundant moisture, and an open sub-soil to carry it off. Yet it will grow to a very handsome tree if these conditions are observed. Very fine effects have been obtained in some places by planting an Araucaria grove. Such an avenue is in fine condition at Woodstock, Co. Kilkenny (running parallel with an avenue of *Abies nobilis*), every tree with its branches intact from turf to summit, and bearing fertile cones. There is a similar, but less perfectly preserved, Araucaria grove at Bicton in Devonshire.

CLASSIFIED INDEX

TO

NATURAL ORDERS, GENERA AND SPECIES

Described in this work.

---

z

INDEX

THE END.

Printed for the Publishers:
The Text by WILLIAM CLOWES & SONS, LTD., London and Beccles;
The Colour Plates by EDMUND EVANS, LTD., London.

Pl. 110.

White Beam—winter.

Pl. 111.

Rowan, or Mountain Ash—summer.